Real change is here.

We understand and are ready
to help you ride the wave.

Wayne T. Glowac

WAYNE GLOWAC
Brand Leader
WAVE Strategy, LLC

HEALTHCARE TSUNAMI

The Wave of Consumerism That Will Change U.S. Business

DEAN HALVERSON and WAYNE GLOWAC

Wave Strategy, LLC
330 S. Whitney Way, Suite 300
Madison, WI 53705
608.232.9696

Printed in the United States of America

ISBN 978-0-9799875-0-2

Acknowledgments

This is our first book, and while we have been dedicated to the process we have also found it to be an adventure. There is much to learn when writing, and we have been fortunate to have a number of great partners in the process. They have contributed much to make this book possible.

First, we have to thank Raechelle Cline, who has served as researcher, editor, and friend. Her knowledge of healthcare, perspective, and resourcefulness have helped us move the book along. Her prodding has kept us on track and on time. Her friendship has made the entire process a pleasant one. We greatly appreciate her contributions.

We must also thank our current and past clients. We have summarized 25 years of experience in this book that our clients enabled us to do. The work has helped us to see the trends and has solidified many of the concepts we have identified in our writing. We have been fortunate to have clients who are not only partners but also friends. They have contributed content and offered viewpoints both in alignment and challenging. This has improved the quality of our writing.

Without our "day jobs" this effort would not have been possible. We are blessed to be surrounded by good people with great ideas at both The Leede Research Group and Glowac, Harris, Madison, Inc. Their work and dedication have allowed us to explore our ideas and evolve our businesses. We appreciate their support and service.

Finally, thanks to our wives, Sheila and Laurie, whose patience, love, and understanding continue to support us in our ongoing entrepreneurial adventures.

We hope you enjoy this work, which has truly been a team effort!

Contents

> Preface

Healthcare is an industry in the midst of significant change. After years of double-digit cost increases, the system has truly reached a breaking point. Where once only employers were heard crying out for change, the call is now coming from all levels of American society. Whether it is business, social service agencies, or government, all understand that the system cannot continue to operate under the current conditions. The voice that is most important to actual change is the quietest of all—that of consumers. They are now feeling the pain and that pain will lead to a new way of doing business.

What some would call *revolution* in U.S. healthcare we believe is actually *evolution*. Evolution is a natural progression of events that is now accelerating. Evolution is a funny thing. Sometimes it moves very slowly with little perceivable change, then suddenly leaps forward with dramatic changes. In the case of the healthcare industry, change has been building for some time, yet it is one of the last industries to fall to the power of consumers. Until now, a third-party- payer system separated the people who paid for the service from the people who used it. For years the only true consumer of healthcare services was the employer. The third-party-payer system allowed the healthcare industry to increase costs at will and resist all efforts to reduce costs. The industry has made significant gains in quality, both from a technical and consumer perspective. Pressure has been building under the surface and it is about to burst with unpredictable outcomes.

As consumers respond to this marketplace, they will do as they have always done: they will vote with their dollars. Their vote will bring some providers to their knees and vault others to the forefront of the industry. Evolution often changes the pecking order, and new players and leaders will likely arise as a result.

At one point in time, employers provided almost three-quarters of American health coverage. That figure is now closer to 60% and even lower in rural areas. As healthcare costs slowly began rising, employers—committed to growth during a booming economy—absorbed the costs. Now, the labor markets have softened as work has been shifted outside the country due to rising costs, including healthcare costs. Employers have reached their limit and are starting to shift costs to their employees. Some employers have dropped out of coverage completely. Cost shifting has occurred both directly and through more subtle changes in plan design, which cause employees to pay higher deductibles and out-of-pocket costs.

As employees assume personal responsibility for costs, they are changing the fundamental model under which health-care has operated for more than 40 years. While this model has not controlled costs, it has allowed for numerous medical innovations in the form of new devices and medications. The system is moving from a third-party-payer model to one that more directly resembles most consumer models seen in other industries today. The progress thus far is barely noticeable. This movement will change the way healthcare is consumed and paid for. It will also lead to dramatic changes in the players who serve these consumers and the way they interact in the healthcare industry.

The new model for healthcare may take years to sort itself out. There are players vying for positions from a number of perspectives. One thing is certain—the new healthcare model will be much more like other consumer product models. The new healthcare model will reward players that deliver a good service at a fair price. It will eliminate those players who cannot meet consumer needs and price points. Volume will be based on actual demand for service, not competitive positioning and filling capacity. New players will offer consumers new ways to meet their needs and save money in the process. This will forever change the business landscape and bring a true consumerism model to healthcare.

This will not be a simple or sweeping change in the industry. When consulting economists with experience in the healthcare industry, we learned that, like most industries, the 80/20 rule applies: 20% of healthcare consumers use 80% of the resources. This group is generally covered under government insurance and is not likely to be impacted by the initial consumerism movement in the United States. We believe, though, that a chain of events set off by the 20% will eventually impact the 80% and create a new model for healthcare.

This book will take you through the history of this change and will demonstrate how pressure has built under the surface for years. We will document how converging trends in multiple industries are creating a wave of change unprecedented in the history of commerce. We will present these ideas and concepts in ways that are logical and understandable whether you are a member of the healthcare industry, a business owner or manager, or a consumer seeking answers for the future. We will also offer a perspective on this new field of healthcare consumerism and differentiate it from past discussions by healthcare professionals.

The goal of this book is to help us all understand the process that has been generating pressure under the surface of healthcare for years. Inside you will find a roadmap to the future of care delivery and a discussion of how consumer forces will change the industry forever. Along with changes in healthcare will come changes in banking, retail and more. The shifting of financial power has ramifications across all segments of industry and for consumers as well. The future will represent a new way of business for many American companies.

Our work indicates that changes in health coverage will move billions of dollars over time from insurers and, to a lesser extent, providers into the hands of consumers, triggering a significant impact on both the insurance and financial services industries. This shift in wealth will impact many segments of the United States economy. Extra dollars in the pockets of consumers will also change healthcare delivery, offering more options and varied ways to receive care.

We believe this wave of change is of a size and scale equal to the force of a tsunami. As this wave crashes through the United States economy it will change the business landscape for years to come. Some players will ride the wave to new-found success, while others will be swept under and away. How will you be affected by the coming tsunami?

❶ What Is a Tsunami?

Today's technology allows little in the world to go unnoticed. The media and Internet unite even the most remote corners of the world. World events are now accessible to all of us at any time. Many of us have heard of tsunamis, the giant waves that hit Japan and other Asian countries. The media easily bring visual proof of the devastation into our homes, and we understand the awesome power and fury of nature.

The scientific definition of a tsunami is an ocean wave produced by a submarine earthquake, landslide, or volcanic eruption. Traditionally an earthquake occurs when two massive plates of earth come together, often moving in opposite directions. This movement builds pressure and eventually results in the tsunami. Tsunami waves start as ripples and eventually can reach enormous dimensions and have sufficient energy to travel across entire oceans.

Tsunamis are an interesting phenomenon. They can wipe clean the landscape or carry along a grass hut and land it safely on a new shore. While some victims are devastated by the impact, others may be swept along to a new life on higher ground because of their ability to ride the wave. Knowing of an impending tsunami can allow potential victims to prepare, keep safe, seek high ground, and set a course for the future.

The same can be said of the business environment. We submit that a business definition of a tsunami is a wave of change produced by subtle changes in business philosophy and consumerism. Such an event would quietly build energy under the surface and then suddenly explode into a wave of change that sweeps through an industry, forever changing the face of business in its wake. As in nature, these events are rare and require several factors to come together perfectly in terms of both direction and timing.

We believe that a tsunami has been building in the healthcare industry for 20 years or more. While the pressure has been clearly visible, much of it went unnoticed or was viewed without concern by the key players in the industry. Lack of action by all involved has led to excessive pressure buildup and the potential for a tsunami-type event has grown.

We believe that today the perfect set of conditions is coming together to trigger a business tsunami. Employers have reached their limits and are shifting costs to employees at an exponentially increasing rate. A fundamental shift in the healthcare market is putting more power into the hands of consumers. As this happens, consumers are quietly taking an active interest in their use of healthcare, working to become better consumers. This new trend will continue to grow as consumers spend their own money on care. Thus, the health-care delivery system as we know it will be forever changed.

As true consumerism comes to the healthcare industry, we will see significant changes in the way healthcare services and products are consumed, delivered, and paid for. This shift to consumerism will generate a wave of change that will impact many key industries in the U.S. economy and shift billions of dollars in the process. As the tsunami builds, a few visionaries are already working to position themselves in the new reformed landscape. Understanding what is going to happen and planning for the future will allow you to do the same.

2 Ground Zero—Pressure Builds

It is hard to believe today that there was ever a time without health insurance. The reality is that in the greater scheme of life and civilization, insurance in most forms is a relatively recent development. Up until well into the 1900s there was truly no need for health insurance. So how did we go from virtually no need for health coverage to it being one of the biggest expenditures in today's economy? That story is the start of the earliest pressure generating the tsunami wave that now appears to be inevitable.

The history of medical care and treatment in the United States generally came from our European roots, where there was a long history of hospitals to care for the sick and needy. Urban healthcare was in its infancy and hospitals were generally part of religious orders set up to care for those who could not care for themselves. Because of their mission, most were considered nonprofit organizations. In the late 1800s healthcare was generally a local service. Country doctors served patients in their own homes. Some doctors were self-taught, while others were educated in large cities or in Europe. In exchange for their services, doctors often accepted goods that ranged from livestock to food products. At that time the average household spent less than 5% of its annual income on healthcare. It was a minor expenditure and thus insurance was not a direct need.

The first insurance plans date back to the Civil War (1861–1865) and were designed to provide specific coverage for accidents related to travel on steamships or trains. The first modern group health plan was formed in 1929 by a group of Dallas, Texas, teachers who, in exchange for a monthly fee, were provided care, room, and board by Baylor Hospital.

Demand was light, as the average consumer spent less than 7% of his or her annual income on healthcare costs in the early 1900s. Coverage was about protecting individuals and families from the potential for financial disaster that could occur if a major health issue arose. The concept did not take off initially, as there was no perceived need.

Traditional life insurers got into the business in the late 1930s and early 1940s. They started offering hospital and disability products that tied into their life insurance lines. It appeared to be a natural fit for insurers to protect the financial position of their clients. Once again, protection from catastrophic loss was the primary offering, and interest in the products began to grow with the addition of dedicated sales forces by the insurers. There was now an active movement in the United States to sell health insurance.

The Great Depression hit the country hard, and hospitals felt the impact too. In 1939, the American Hospital Association began allowing insurance plans that met specific standards to use the Blue Cross name and logo. Blue Cross plans were not treated as insurance since they were owned by hospitals and were given nonprofit status. Physicians became worried that these plans would expand to physicians' services, and they formed their own plan, Blue Shield, in 1946. By 1945 Blue Cross had captured 59% of the health insurance market.

"The Blues" began to meet a growing demand for coverage. As hospitals took a more passive political stance, the Blues emerged as the primary intermediary between their clients and the government. Very soon these two large nonprofit insurance companies, Blue Cross (hospital) and Blue Shield (physician), grew to become the largest managed care industry in history.

The 1940s were a time of great growth in this country and also a time of war. Businesses were prospering and were struggling to find the employees they needed to continue to grow. This was due in part to government regulations that limited the growth of wages that employers could pay. Employers needed to find tools to help retain their existing employees and attract new ones. The concept of employee benefits was born and grew rapidly from that point. This gave employers who offered such benefits a competitive advantage in gaining quality employees. It also gave the employees a new tool to cover their payment of health costs.

Health coverage became a low-cost benefit for employees and was effective in both retention and attraction. As more employers joined the coverage bandwagon, basic offerings became less effective as a competitive tool. Coverage was now available from the majority of employers. Employers needed new offerings to achieve their goals, and the insurance industry was more than happy to increase the depth of its products for employers. This was the beginning of a long and continual process of changing insurance from the catastrophic protection tool it was originally designed to be to a benefit that many in our country have come to believe is a right for all and one that could never be taken away.

As time progressed, a combination of employer demand and insurance industry marketing moved health coverage to a benefit that covered virtually all costs that a consumer might incur. In 1954, the Internal Revenue Services (IRS) solidified prepaid insurance when it initiated code that allowed employers to deduct health insurance payments. This enactment was driven by labor organizations seeking better care for their members and by government organizations that often set the bar with their high-benefit programs. While these groups certainly meant no harm, their actions set off a chain of events that would impact every industry in this country and lead to our current situation.

Now, more than 50 years later, employers in many cases have reached their limit. Double-digit annual increases in health insurance costs over the past 10 years have changed the foundation of business. Rising health costs have impacted the use of business resources and ur competitiveness in the world market. Employers have dealt with incremental cost increases for many years and have tried to make decisions that are good for both employees and business. This effort, albeit honorable, has become increasingly difficult.

Many employers feel they can no longer afford their current healthcare financing role and are shifting more of the cost burden to individual employees. They have done this by increasing the employee share of premiums and making other adjustments to plans that cause individuals to pay more. Generally speaking, employers do not think that their employees are good users of health services and have contributed significantly to rising costs by misusing services and failing to take care of their own overall health. Some figures estimate that up to 70% of healthcare costs are driven by issues tied to unhealthy lifestyles. While employers have tried wellness programs, most employees have failed to participate and employers are now beginning to push the issue.

Who is to blame? As consumers, we must bear a significant portion of the blame for our current situation. We have taken healthcare for granted, believing it is something that is not frequently used and most often is an inconvenience. We stay away from the doctor's office, waiting until something is wrong or some other action forces us to visit the doctor.

www.cartoonstock.com

We live in a system that provides compensation for the wrong reasons. Insurers and providers are not paid to make us healthy. They are paid to take care of us when we are sick. The more people who are sick, the more money the insurers and providers make. There are many experts who say there has to be a fundamental shift in the paradigm of care before we can truly address the healthcare system of the future. This is starting in some settings and will lead to a better design in the future. When we as consumers do need services, our basic goal is simple—get in and get out as quickly as possible. We want relief from pain or symptoms, with minimal personal inconvenience. We do not understand how the healthcare system works and how we should prepare before we go. We

fumble through the appointment process or head to walk-in clinics to avoid setting an appointment altogether.
Our employers provide our insurance, and we have had that benefit for as long as we can remember. We don't always understand the difference between insurance plas and the care they cover. We seldom put any significant thought into the type of insurance coverage we have unless our employer has forced us to make plan selections or we have been forced to seek coverage on our own. Even then, we most commonly rely on recommendations of friends or family members to make our selection.

We are not much more particular about our use of health services. We are likely to have a perceived relationship with a physician even though we may not have seen him or her for 10 years. Once again, our physician choice was likely a recommendation from friends or family. We basically go along with whatever our physician and other healthcare professionals tell us. We question little about the services we are provided. If the doctor indicates we need a test, we get the test. Cost has never been a factor in our decisions until very recently.

We have never understood costs in healthcare. We understand that a premium is paid, and, in some cases, we pay a portion of it. We also understand that there are some things that we have to pay for ourselves until we reach our deductible. We are not always sure what the deductible is and what qualifies. We never ask our providers about what things cost and don't believe they would actually be able to tell us if we did.

Lack of financial accountability has enabled many of us to overuse or incorrectly use the system. When we are not responsible for payment of services, we are more likely to abuse the normal process of service selection. Too many of us rush to the physician's office or even the hospital emergency room for moderate signs or symptoms that may not require any medical assistance.

One exception occurs when we have a major health emergency or if someone in our household has a chronic condition. Some consumers then become immersed in the healthcare industry, conducting extensive research, often on the Internet, and questioning doctors. Only then do patient and physician conduct a healthy dialogue about a care plan and expected outcomes.

However, only a few of us with chronic conditions generate major annual expenditures. An estimated 88% of Americans use less than $500 in actual healthcare services annually outside of their insurance premiums. This represents about 20% of the total costs spent in healthcare each year. Nine percent of Americans incur between $500 and $40,000 annually. While this is a wide range it still represents only 30% of the annual spending. A mere 2.5% of individuals spend more than $40,000 per year and represent *half* the spending on healthcare. This inverse pyramid is what drives the current system for both insurance and care.

Consumer spending on healthcare is as much as 40% of a household's annual income, according to some government figures. In the period between 2000 and 2005, health insurance premiums increased a total of 63%, or just over 10% annually. A 2007 Commonwealth Fund study indicates that the fastest-rising costs were administrative on the insurance side and pharmaceutical spending on the service side. Medication costs are increasing at a rate faster than that of traditional services. During the same time period, overall inflation was less than 4% and earnings generally increased about 4% annually. The net result was that the percent of wages spent on premiums alone became a far more significant portion of earnings than ever before in our history.

This was not the first time consumers experienced double-digit increases in premium costs. In a three-year period between 1988 and 1990, insurance premiums increased a total of 44%, or better than 14% per year. The exorbitant increase led to a call for national healthcare in the United States, defined as health coverage provided and paid for by the government. This call has never fully materialized, as legislators and the medical profession cannot agree on a model that all believe would function well and save money in the process.

While arguments for national healthcare are still made, there does not appear to be a perfect model of healthcare in any of the first-world countries. While Canada and the U.K. have nationalized systems that offer affordable care, they are far from perfect. Both systems use complicated evaluation processes to determine the value of treatment procedures, and many needs go unmet for months if not longer. As a result, medical tourism to the United States and other countries has increased dramatically, giving rise to a whole new industry. Some U.S.-based clinics are flying in patients from Canada to meet needs that patients are willing to pay for out of their own pockets.

What is more concerning than our delivery model in comparison to others around the world is what we spend on healthcare. The Commonwealth Fund study notes that the United States spends 16% of its gross domestic product (GDP) on healthcare, compared to 8% to 10% in most other industrialized nations. The Centers for Medicare and Medicaid Services (CMS) estimates that healthcare spending will continue to outpace GDP for the next 10 years, ultimately exceeding $4 trillion. We are currently spending more than twice the amount per capita spent by any other industrialized nation, yet our overall health ratings are lower than those of many of these same countries.

Then there is the issue of underinsured or uninsured Americans. The Commonwealth Fund study indicates that almost 45 million Americans have no insurance coverage at all. Researchers believe another possible 16 million exist who would be considered underinsured because of high out-of-pocket costs compared to their income. The study also indicates that women are more heavily impacted by underinsurance than men.

The care and treatment of these underinsured and uninsured citizens is a heated issue, bringing to the surface the some-

www.cartoonstock.com

what taboo issue of an organization's mission as it relates to healthcare. Two clearly defined segments in healthcare networks are seen in faith-based versus non-faith-based provider networks.

Historically, religious orders brought healthcare to many rural and impoverished communities. They provided care when no one else would. They would treat anyone who came to their facilities, regardless of ability to pay. Even today, many faith-based organizations adhere to this mission.

Conversely, most non-faith-based provider networks treat healthcare as a business. While some provide uncompensated care as a public service, many do not feel obligated to provide care for those without resources. While they are obligated to care for those in emergency settings, as provided by the Emergency Medical Treatment and Active Labor Act (EMTALA), they often send patients with nonurgent conditions and without coverage (and even those with Medicare or Medicaid) to their religious counterparts. This practice of off-loading unprofitable patients often goes unnoticed, yet it is a practice that is common in today's marketplace.

Off-loading unprofitable business is a good decision in any industry. Healthcare is no different. Off-loading does, however, place a significant financial burden on the faith-based counterparts. In many small and mid-sized markets, competition is generally between faith-based and non-faith-based provider networks. The added financial pressure is significant when the industry goes through crunch times.

Until 1997, a mechanism existed to fund care for those without the ability to pay. This was called Hill-Burton care and was based on a 1946 act of Congress. The U.S. government provided the healthcare industry with grants and loans, which were used for modernization and construction projects. In return, facilities would provide a certain amount of free, or charity, care for those in need.

Consumers were able to apply at the admissions office for this type of coverage, and the provider system would offer coverage if they met the specific criteria of the program. While about 300 facilities are still obligated to provide this care, the program is no longer a functional tool to care for those without coverage. This burden now falls on the provider community and government through social service organizations. The religious provider networks often supplement their operations through funds raised in their other missions. This lack of coverage and added pressure of costs is causing financial hardship to some of these religious networks.

We have heard the call for a national plan again recently as the nation struggles to deal with rising healthcare costs. President George W. Bush made healthcare a major initiative for the future in his 2007 State of the Union address. He proposed moving to a standardized tax deduction for the purchase of private health insurance. The deduction strategy is intended to give lower-income taxpayers greater incentive to purchase private-market insurance. A significant focus of the president's proposal is to drive more people into the private market. He also developed a number of initiatives designed to support individual state efforts to promote greater coverage.

Republican candidates in the 2008 presidential campaign have already hinted that they, too, will offer a national plan to move millions from employer-sponsored insurance to individual coverage. Like President Bush, they believe that forcing consumers into the open market will help solve the long-term ills of the healthcare industry.

Leading Democrats have favored an approach in which government takes over the health insurance system, similar to the system in Canada, for example. Universal healthcare, distinguished from national healthcare, would be provided through individual states or through a federal program. All citizens would be entitled to universal coverage, creating the largest available pool to share risk. The Democrats have recently softened their position, moving to a more business-friendly model. The two sides clearly differ on the approach and the ability of government to impact change and future costs.

States are getting into the act as well. Wisconsin governor Jim Doyle in 2007 proposed the Wisconsin Health Plan, which would cover all citizens of the state through a payroll tax ranging from 8% to 12%, shared by employer and employee. His team believes that this, combined with available federal funding for Medicaid and affiliated programs, could generate $13.5 billion and would save the state $500 million in Medicaid spending.

In California, Governor Arnold Schwarzenegger has offered a $12 billion universal health coverage plan of his own. His plan would force all residents to have insurance and all insurance companies to accept all customers, even those with medical problems. Those employers that do not offer coverage would be charged an additional 4% payroll tax that would go to a state fund to subsidize those who cannot afford coverage. The plan has raised some eyebrows as it calls for fees to be paid by doctors and hospitals.

California has the largest number of uninsured residents, estimated to be 6.8 million people, or 18.8% of the population. While Texas and Florida have higher percentages of uninsured, their actual numbers are smaller. The healthcare industry in California tops $208 billion annually. Republicans, in the minority in both houses in California, are competing with a Democratic plan that is similar to that of Wisconsin. The Democratic plan calls for heavier payroll contributions by employers to provide universal coverage. It does not call for fees to be paid by the healthcare industry. Meanwhile the insurance industry in California is not taking any change lying down. It is running media campaigns warning that making changes to the existing private insurance industry would be "ill-considered reforms." It is using a media campaign similar to one that upended the national healthcare plan promoted by Hillary Clinton in 1994.

In 2006, the state of Massachusetts also passed a universal coverage plan. This plan was more tolerable to the business community as it tapped a state fund already established for care of the uninsured. The plan put only a modest additional burden on employers, with a $295 per employee fee if an employer did not offer coverage. However, newspaper coverage already indicates a backlash by physicians, who are leaving the state because of lower reimbursements and impact on their livelihood.

Healthcare is clearly a major issue for the 2008 elections. The primary difference between Democrat and Republican plans is who should be responsible for driving the change. The Democrats believe that government is the key to solving the problem. The Republicans believe the market can fix itself if government gets out of the way.

Concurrently, other expenses are emptying consumer wallets, including rising interest rates and fuel costs. Many consumers lured into large mortgages in the 1990s now find they have more home than they need, bigger payments than they can afford, and a home that is not selling under current rates. While the government tells us that inflation is under control, calculations do not take into account other risings costs that can take a major toll on personal finances.

Whether a person is healthy or has some medical issues, a significant portion of his or her earnings are being paid toward health insurance coverage. While an individual will see the direct dollars that are paid in premiums, another more significant amount is paid by the employer. These funds go to insurers to cover care and manage large reserves that they are required to hold. Overall, this contributes to the increases as insurers add profits to the equation.

Some projections indicate that if healthcare premiums continue to rise at the current rate, costs could exceed total income by as early as 2020, right when the baby boomers will move a large group of patients through the Medicare ranks. Under current trends, Medicare costs to government are expected to double by the year 2015. Clearly we are on a course that cannot continue without triggering a significant event. We believe that event will be the Healthcare Tsunami.

3 When Is a Consumer Not a Consumer?

This is an interesting question with a simple answer. A consumer is not a consumer when he or she does not pay for the product he or she uses. The definition of consumption assumes that some form of remuneration is provided in exchange for the product or service used. When this does not occur, a true consumer model does not exist. In most industry segments, consumers vote with their wallets. Success is determined, in part, by counting those dollars in sales. Typically, the most successful products generate the most dollars or share of the market. This is not possible in today's healthcare model, but that day may now be on the horizon.

Employees with employer-provided coverage have enjoyed a luxurious position in the use of healthcare services. An employer provides a "magic card" that allows access to healthcare services. This card has few limitations related to choice, cost, or the way services are used. Employees receive the care they feel they need, where and when they need it. They give little consideration to cost or utilization of services. There is no reason; they are not paying the bill other than simple out-of-pocket costs. Even that process is sometimes counterproductive. The faster they spend to the deductible, the faster coverage reaches 100%. Some consumers, therefore, do not worry about costs.

The healthcare industry is truly unique in today's economy. It is one of the only industry segments in which the consumer of the products and services is not the same as the one who pays for it. It is the last major industry segment, outside government, that has not given in to the will of consumers. Employers continue to carry the majority of the costs related to the healthcare of their employees. In today's environment, employees are paying more than they ever have in the history of healthcare finance. Employees absorb about one-third, while insurance or an employer absorbs the remaining two-thirds of healthcare costs. The consumer's share is growing and will continue to grow in the years ahead. Our recent work indicates that many consumers expect to personally pay up to half of their healthcare costs in the next five years. Even if this does not happen, the sheer power of the perception will generate change.

A disconnect exists between the delivery of healthcare and the payment for the service. While many workers pay for at least some of their healthcare through payroll deductions for premiums and deductibles, that payment has very little correlation to personal use of healthcare services.

This type of consumer model does not generally function well over time. When users do not pay for a product, they generally do not value it. When they do not value it, they often do not take care to make good decisions about it and do not use the product efficiently. They also tend to overuse the product, as there is no incentive to conserve. All of these are major factors in the current position of healthcare in the United States.

The healthcare industry has benefited, in a business sense, tremendously from the lack of a consumer model for many years. One obvious benefit is that since the actual users did not pay for the services used, consumers did not place any great importance on price. Since consumers only paid a small fraction of their insurance or coverage costs, they also did not place importance on the cost of insurance. Consumer apathy has allowed the double-digit increases that have taken place consistently over the past 10 years.

For many years, a volleying of blame has taken place for rising costs. Some years it was the fault of the insurance industry. In other years it was the fault of the providers. Today, employers see plenty of blame to go around, all of which is outside outside their control.

The healthcare industry has also benefited from the lack of a true consumer from a delivery standpoint. The delivery of healthcare for many years was impacted by capacity and production. Providers had no real limits on utilization, so their main focus was on managing the "production" of care and treatment. They could fill the capacity their system had available.

Since the end users of the product were not paying for the service, consumers also did not have a high level of expectations around the delivery of that service. This meant that long waiting times, lack of personable care, and a variety of other customer-service ills were accepted by patients and, to a certain extent, still are. It was an acceptable exchange since they were not paying for the care.

This focus changed as the quality movement hit healthcare and competition for employers and their employees forced change. The quality movement has fixed most of the operational issues that plagued the healthcare industry for the past 20 years, such as delivering hot meals and fixing delays and flaws in the admissions process. The notion of quality moved the industry from being behind to being competitive with other segments offering top quality through movements like ISO certification, Lean and Six Sigma tools.

What has been slower in developing is the healthcare industry's focus on the relationship they have with the patient/consumer. Industry leaders now understand that as processes, like the delivery of hot meals, were fixed, the patient's focus moved on to other matters. These tended to be the relationships they have with people in the delivery system. Our research shows that the most important asset a provider has in its business is the relationship between primary care physicians and their patients. This relationship offers the ability to steer patients and direct them through the provider network. There is some evidence, though, that the strength of this relationship has already peaked and may be declining. The value of relationships will continue to grow as consumers begin to vote more directly with their dollars.

For the past 40 years or more, the true consumers of healthcare services have been employers. They have paid for the majority of care and treatment. They have absorbed the burden of rising healthcare and coverage costs. Employers have quickly responded, as most consumers will, in a rising cost environment and have tried to control costs and cut spend-

"Prepare a list of our employees who go outside to smoke. Our healthcare costs are too high so I want to know who to let go."

www.cartoonstock.com

ing. The challenge is that they can be only partially effective in that process since they have little or no control over the way their employees use healthcare services. They also found that they have very little control over the price of both insurance and care delivery.

Most employer work to date has focused on controlling costs by leveraging providers and insurers to discount the price of services for their employees. Employers increasingly turned to managed care, which was designed to keep tighter controls on access and use of services, and offered wellness and prevention programs to improve overall employee health and reduce long-term costs.

Historically, employers provided almost 75% of coverage in the United States. While that number has declined in recent years, employers still carry more than 60% of coverage in most states. The decline is due to employers reaching a breaking point for employee healthcare costs. Some employers have eliminated coverage entirely, while others have quietly shifted more of the cost burden to employees. Corporate spending cuts, changes in workforce demographics, and a softer economy in recent years readied the environment for this transition. As the practice of cost shifting became more accepted by larger employers, the process accelerated. This transition may be the most important factor in the coming tsunami and the changes in United States healthcare.

Current trends show strong growth in what are known as high-deductible health plans. While comprising only a small portion of current coverage, high-deductible health plans are projected to consume as much as 25% of the market by 2010. Often referred to as consumer-directed health plans (CDHPs), these plans are designed with deductibles between $1,500 and $5,500. Traditional plans generally have deductibles under the $1,000 mark. High-deductible plans are frequently supplemented with a health reimbursement account (HRA) or the newer health savings account (HSA). Both accounts allow employers and employees to contribute funds to cover the cost of needed medical care not covered by insurance.

All this action is getting the attention of consumers/employees. For the first time, they are taking a more active interest in the way they use healthcare. They are suddenly feeling the pain of rising costs and becoming frustrated with the higher out-of-pocket spending. Consumers are now starting to understand that employers can no longer cover costs that increase without control annually. They are also starting to understand their need to be good consumers of health services. Some are realizing that if they don't spend on healthcare now, they are able to save those resources for future needs. Slowly but surely, consumers are beginning to purchase healthcare services and products much like they do other products and services.

When consumers do not pay for something, they are not consumers. They are receiving a gift. While gifts are wonderful things, the current environment requires that we make healthcare and related coverage a typical consumer product.

When consumers spend their own money, they generally make better usage decisions over time.

We will never have all the population interested in the issue of healthcare costs because more than a quarter of coverage is provided through Medicare, Medicaid, and other government programs. While this system is under great financial pressure, it is not likely that its users will have enough incentive to become strong consumers. Likewise, those with significant financial resources may not care much about how well they consume healthcare services.

Not everyone agrees that we should have a true consumer model for the best long-term success of the industry. Some critics believe that putting the decisions in the hands of consumers and giving them financial incentive to not spend their money is a formula for disaster. They also believe consumers will waive care and screening of minor issues to save money and miss early diagnoses that would save money on more serious conditions down the road. Critics have predicted that patients will not always select the most appropriate care and treatment when cost is a significant factor in consideration.

For now, we do not know who is right or wrong. No major comparative studies have been completed with the new consumers who will be spending their own dollars. These will certainly begin in the near future.

Most of us, though, will continue to feel pressure to become better healthcare consumers. We will quickly learn that spending our own money is different than spending some-one else's. We will find that as we move to HSAs we will pay more attention to what we spend and how we spend it. We will also come to understand that dollars saved today are not only available for tomorrow, but will reduce our future costs by reducing insurance costs as we can increase deductibles. Although the full force of the healthcare tsunami is not yet upon us, we are starting to feel its impact.

4 What if Other Industries Acted Like Healthcare?

What is so unique about healthcare? Surely other industries must have similar models. The reality is that the third-party-payer format is one that is not seen in any other segment of the economy. The free-market system has determined that the best way to run an industry is to allow market forces to come into play and let consumers make decisions based on their needs and budgets. While government intervenes in many industries and creates some limitations to protect open competition, most markets are consumer driven.

A business associate of ours looked at the current healthcare system and made a simple analogy. He said, "What if our employer paid for our groceries? Do you think that some of the hotdogs and macaroni and cheese that were in our carts would be replaced by steak and shrimp?" This perspective is indicative of the problems we have under the current healthcare system.

Let's contrast healthcare to another large-scale American industry, the automotive industry. Automobiles have insurance coverage designed to cover costs related to repair in the event of an accident. Vehicles may also have extended warranties that cover the costs of non-accident repairs needed on the vehicle, generally for larger items such as engine and drive train. Extended warranties tend to cover catastrophic problems with the vehicle, not everyday wear and tear.

On the surface, this would appear to be a very close analogy to healthcare in today's market, but with one significant difference: the automobile market has a direct-payer system. The people (drivers) who use the product (cars) or services

(insurance or extended warranties) are the ones who actually pay for it. So while there is a resemblance to healthcare, the automotive industry is still a true consumer market—one in which consumers vote with their dollars to impact available products and services and the players that offer them.

Let's put the automotive industry into a truly comparable perspective with the healthcare industry. In this comparison, when you purchase an automobile, your employer would offer you an employee benefit that covered that vehicle for its entire life or your duration of employment. This would include traditional automotive insurance and would also create an extended warranty program covering major failures of that vehicle during your ownership. To be truly comparable, the coverage would also offer routine maintenance of the vehicle, based on whatever perceived needs you had as an owner. In fact, in some cases it would even cover things like cosmetic care, allowing you to change the color of your vehicle, add accessories, or even change the interior configuration. Your share of this coverage would be only a small percentage of the total cost paid as a monthly contribution.

If this scenario existed in the automotive industry, what would happen? It is easy to see that the ramifications for cost would be significant. If the owner of the car does not have to pay for its care and treatment, a couple of issues arise. First, the incentive to maintain the vehicle is diminished. Vehicle owners would experience few downsides to letting the vehicle rust away or break down because at some point, when it became bad enough, they could take the vehicle in and have it repaired as good as new at someone else's expense. Owners might even ignore simple, low-cost maintenance, such as oil changes and tune-ups, because if the engine wore out, they could simply ask for a new one. Furthermore, there would be no incentive to comply with vehicle care recommendations because failures of the vehicle would be repaired anyway.

On the flip side, perhaps the lack of personal responsibility for costs would lead vehicle owners to over use services. If plans were to cover such things as car washes, perhaps they would wash their cars more often. Some drivers might change the oil every 1,500 miles if it didn't cost anything. Annual vehicle checkups could be a strong opportunity for service centers with extensive diagnostics because cost would not be a consideration for vehicle owners. Today, we do not generally see automotive service centers widely open 24

"Say ahhhh."

hours per day. Those that provide after-hours service charge a premium for that convenience. Do you think there might be greater incentive to offer these services if providers knew they could charge at will for them without complaints from the users?

In this scenario there would be ramifications in two key areas. The first would be the cost of the automobile itself. The change in the system would have some level of influence on the purchasing cycle for automobiles. If owners were able to take better care of their vehicles without significant personal cost, vehicles would likely last longer. Therefore, the percentage of people replacing vehicles due to mechanical issues and needs would decline, thus reducing overall demand. In most production systems, declining demand tends to increase unit pricing, as the producer needs to cover fixed costs related to production. The cost of a vehicle would then increase. The change to a service-driven environment might make it more attractive for the automobile industry to service vehicles rather than produce them. This would significantly change its business mode by reducing models, options, and choice.

The other key area would be the cost of insurance and other types of vehicle-related coverage. Remember that in this scenario the employer is paying for insurance coverage. The addition of more "benefits" in the plan design is likely to dramatically increase the cost. Add to this the fact that vehicles might cost more in this environment, and we can clearly see a scenario of rapidly increasing coverage costs that would be difficult to control. Just as in healthcare, the employer would have little control over how the employee cared for his or her car or used services related to it. The automotive industry would have difficulty surviving in the long term under this scenario. We would see a similar pattern of concern on the part of employers as their costs increase at a rate that is unmanageable within their budgets.

While we cannot literally equate your life or that of a family member to an automobile, the stark difference between healthcare and other industries is clear. This is true even in environments that have strong insurance components that impact the user of the related products and services. We would never expect to realize this scenario in the automotive market. Why do we believe that healthcare should be delivered by this method?

Accepting the problems with the current model will help us to understand why the tsunami is coming and the significant impact it will have on the future.

5 Insurance—A Benefit? A Right? A Player?

We have already reviewed the history of health insurance in the United States and the chain of events that has led us to our current position. The business of insurance is basically one of transferring risk. The customer determines his or her level of comfort with different risks. The insurer steps in and is willing to take on the additional risk in return for compensation. Most of us will take as little risk as possible in our lives, especially when it comes to our finances. This and employer-provided coverage set up the perfect environment for the health insurance industry.

We also have an environment in which the competitive nature of employment in this country, combined with the development of products in the insurance industry, creates a very robust health system. Unions played a key role in the creation process, using their power to negotiate deeper health benefit plans over time. Many of these plans provided coverage for employees not only during their employment, but also for the rest of their lives. This has created a significant level of financial liabilities for companies that did not plan for or fully understand the budget ramifications. For example, more than $1,000 of revenue from every GM vehicle is used to pay for health insurance for employees who no longer work for General Motors.

According to the United States Census Bureau, insurance today is still dominated by employer-provided coverage—for approximately 60% of the population. The government provides another 27% through Medicare and Medicaid. About 7% of consumers purchase their insurance directly. The balance have no insurance coverage. We have seen a shift in coverage with the employer covering fewer people and the government covering more. Some of this is the result of an aging society and the Medicare program providing coverage. Some is based on employers dropping coverage due to cost issues.

Employer-provided coverage has changed dramatically in the past 10 years. Historically, a person often worked for a single employer for his or her entire adult life. Generational employment was not uncommon, with two and even three generations of family members working for the same employer. That process created a structure that bonded the employee to the employer forever. It is also part of what created the significant benefit plans that changed the perspective of society. Over time, we have come to believe that these are not benefits but are actually our right as individuals who live and work in the United States.

Global competition is forcing us to change our perspective. Today companies are doing more with less. This is true whether it is management or production staff. Companies have been forced to use more part-time and temporary help in order to maximize the value of their stock prices and stay competitive with other countries that offer substantially less in terms of wages and benefits.

Some will argue that the cost of healthcare coverage for employees played a significant role in the movement of more jobs overseas and the use of more part-time and temporary help by United States employers. In competing with production in third-world countries, there was not only the difference in wages but also the lack of benefits in those countries that accentuated our current situation.

Few of us work at the same company our parents did. In fact, many of us now in the workforce will in our lifetime. Many even change careers a number of times, a practice that is projected to increase in the next 20 years. Employers are no longer looking out for our lives, but rather working to maximize their profitability and stock values, which results in significant changes to all benefits, including health coverage.

Traditional, indemnity-type insurance plans are no longer the norm in employer circles. These have been replaced by a wide variety of plans such as health maintenance organizations (HMOs) and preferred provider organizations (PPOs). Both were attempts to reduce employer costs by leveraging buying power, reducing choice, and tightening the reins on utilization. HMOs, PPOs and managed care in general have fallen out of favor with employees because of the many restrictions inherent in the system.

Unfortunately, neither of these plan types met the goal of successfully controlling healthcare costs, which has caused

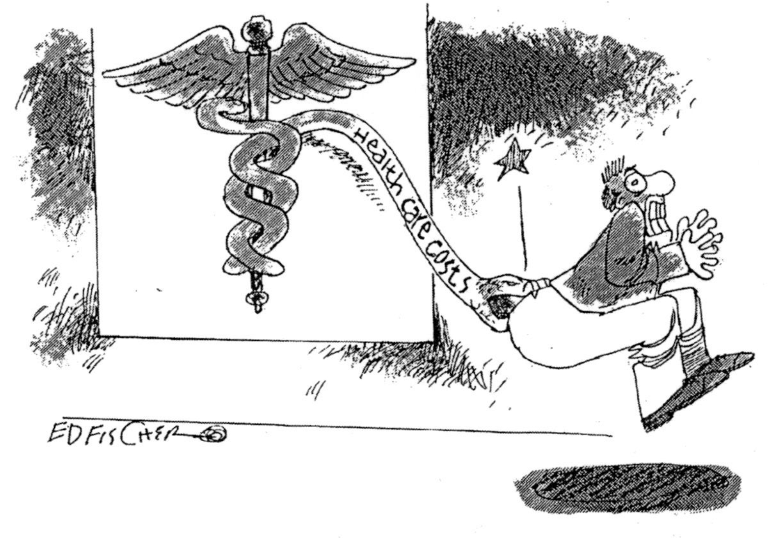

www.cartoonstock.com

a backlash from employers as well. Double-digit increases brought new calls from employers for plans that would reduce costs both immediately and in the long term.

Some now are questioning the value of tying health insurance to employment. They cite the portable nature of today's work environment, and believe that insurance should be tied to the individual, not his or her employer. This would increase portability and reduce added costs that can be generated by changes in jobs and lapses in coverage. This is logical and may be another paradigm shift that will be required to truly change the future of healthcare.

Some estimates indicate that poor lifestyle choices are the root cause of 50% to 70% of healthcare costs. Studies indicate that the cost of poor health is two to three times higher than medical costs. These same studies also note that up to 30% of care provided to patients would technically be deemed unnecessary. Ultimately, work done by all the players in the past 30 years has not generated improvements in key areas of the true costs of healthcare. But it has lead to the recent and rapid growth of consumer-directed health plans (CDHPs).

CDHPs are commonly referred to as high-deductible health plans (HDHP) and generally include some type of health savings account or health reimbursement account. CDHP lower premium costs by placing a higher burden of risk on the policyholder. In this setting, the individual insured party is responsible for paying for all of his or her care up to a deductible, which would typically be as high as $5,500 for an individual, and up to $11,000 for a family. This is significantly more risk than most consumers are willing to take under traditional managed care policies that offer deductibles of $500 to $1,000 for individuals.

HDHPs are considered one of the hottest products in the insurance industry today. As of 2007, these plans were held by 6 to 8 million people and are expected to grow significantly in the next three to five years as employers seek ways to reduce their overall costs. Some believe that a quarter of the privately insured marketplace will have this type of plan by 2010. A recently completed study of Fortune 1000 employers by industry leader Fiserv Health indicates that 48% of their employees could be covered under such plans in the next three years. Therefore, we can confidently surmise that HDHPs and HSAs will play a significant role in the future of the healthcare market and the size and speed of the pending tsunami.

To offset financial risk, legislation was created that allows individuals to purchase health savings accounts (HSA). HSAs allow an individual to make contributions of tax-free dollars to cover future expenses. An employer may also make contributions to this account. An individual can make total annualaccount contributions of $2,850 and a family can deposit as much as $5,650 into an HSA. Recent rule changes now allow a one-time transfer of up to one year of funding from a current individual retirement account (IRA) or retirement account to cover the gap between contributions and the deductible in the early years of the account. This will rise in 2008 to $2,900 per individual and $5,900 per family due to IRS rule changes.

Estimates from the Kaiser Family Foundation and Forrester Research indicate that as many as 8 million individuals are covered under CDHPs. Movement to these plans is strongest in the largest companies, with an estimated 32% of those employing more than 5,000 employees offering such plans in 2005.

The first question that comes to many consumers' minds is why they would want to take on added risk in their health coverage. The answer is that funds not used in these HSAs can be retained and carried over for future years. Those that are not used at all can be applied to retirement needs, whether health related or not.

As the size of an account grows, consumers have the flexibility to increase deductibles in order to lower premiums. In time, proponents hope that deductible limits will increase to accommodate the growing funds that could be built by young, healthy consumers.

Many believe that CDHPs are the secret to controlling the rising cost of healthcare. If consumers spend their own dollars, they will be better consumers of healthcare services. If they are rewarded by keeping the dollars they do not use, they will be more cognizant of the decisions they make, and eliminate duplication in testing and services that cost millions annually.

Mercer Human Resource Consulting indicates that in 2006, the percentage of employers offering CDHPs more than tripled. Its research further indicates that 16% of employees will select such plans when available. These statistics do not take into account employers that do not offer a choice, but simply make a CDHP their primary offering.

Mercer's work indicates that in 2006 the average cost to employers for health coverage and related costs was $7,523 per employee, representing a 6.1% increase from the prior year. This was the second straight year of such increases. The average cost of those employers with CDHPs was $5,480, 18% lower than the cost of traditional PPO plans. Employers will clearly embrace opportunities to reduce costs as evidenced by this work.

President Bush has joined the growing list of supporters of this approach.

> *I strongly believe that the United States Congress needs to strengthen health savings accounts, just like they need to make sure that the tax code treats every person in America fairly. And that's why I've suggested we change the tax code to enable the small business owner, the self-employed, or the individual worker to be able to have more affordable insurance. There's a lot we can do together to empower the individual in this country to be in charge of his or her health-care decisions.*
>
> — President George W. Bush, April 2, 2007

His proposal presents an interesting concept and one that makes a great deal of sense. For years, employers have had the option of basically doing the same thing by being self-insured. They have worked the margin between expected claims and coverage costs and have taken on a certain amount of risk within the company rather than selling it to the insurance providers. Employers bring together a number of insurance products to do this, including a product called stop-loss coverage, which is designed to limit their maximum risk as an organization.

Why should employees and consumers not have the same opportunity as employers? After all, it would give employees/consumers the opportunity to make the best financial decisions for their families and themselves. It would also help build wealth, not only for them, but for future generations as well. Finally, it would put them in control and provide them with incentives to be healthy. It is now up to government to give them the latitude to make these larger decisions down the road.

Plans cannot currently offer deductibles of more than $5,500. This means that personal stop-loss coverage would require a change in the current legislation relating to CDHPs. We believe the growing HSAs and consumer pressure, along with the insurance industry's desire to find new products to replace lost revenue, will lead to future change in this area.

Tom Rogala, a licensed insurance broker in the state of Michigan, is considered an expert on the HSA phenomenon. His materials outline his belief that an HSA option can benefit just about everyone, whether employer or employee.

Rogala is also a proponent of employers not only getting rates for group HSA accounts, but also for individual coverage. He has found that rates for individual plans are often as much as 40% lower than group plans for younger or healthier individuals. This is based, in part, on coverage requirements that employers must offer but individuals can opt out of, such as maternity care and/or specific coverage limits. The challenge to these plans has been the lack of guaranteed issue, which allows coverage for anyone regardless of their current health condition or a preexisting condition.

CDHPs coupled with HSAs may not work for larger employers, as they will have employees who may be rejected or cause up-rating due to current medical conditions or other factors. Unfortunately, this often means that healthy employees pay more for those on the team who are not healthy. This is not the case with individual plans. So, more employees are exploring options that allow them to find cost-effective care outside their employer-provided plans.

The state of Michigan is providing a unique pilot project to demonstrate the value of individual HSAs with guaranteed issue. A program by Blue Cross Blue Shield of Michigan called Flexible Blue offers guaranteed HSA coverage with a CDHP for only $167 per month for *either* an individual or family. The plan not only offers an incredibly low premium, it also provides up to $500 annually in preventive care per person covered under the plan and offers maternity care and dental options.

Rogala recently quoted rates for a six-person group in Michigan under three scenarios. He found that a traditional group co-pay plan would generate premiums of between $2,633 and $4,222 per participant, dependent upon underwriting. This compared to group HSA/HDHP rates that ranged from $2,160 to $2,503. Finally, the same six people on individual

HSA/HDHP plans would generate premiums of between $1,222 and $1,759. As you can see, there are significant differences in the costs associated with coverage.

Michigan is the only state, as of this writing, that offers guaranteed-coverage HSA accounts. Therefore, the previous example would not be applicable to other states, especially for those who may have existing medical conditions. The example does, however, show the potential savings that could be generated by looking at alternative coverage models. It also demonstrates that affordable care is available under the right plan designs.

As much as one-third of HSA-type coverage is now sold to those who were formerly uninsured. This is an indication that with the right products in the marketplace, the system of products and consumers does have the potential to address much of the issue of the uninsured. Government should be looking for ways to help this process along without disrupting the forces that generated it.

The concept of individual HSAs versus group or employer-provided plans could become a political issue in the 2008 presidential elections. One prominent Republican presidential candidate announced a health plan that seeks to move millions of employees from employer coverage to individual policies. He believes that personal responsibility is a key to solving our current healthcare dilemma.

A larger question arises if this trend continues. The logical participants in these CDHPs are those who are young and/or healthy. They have the best opportunity to build significant account balances and take greater control of their financial future as it relates to healthcare. The question then becomes, what will happen to the rest of the population?

Remember that the concept of insurance is basically one built on shared risk. In a large population, most will be healthy and some will be sick at any given time. Actuaries make projections about the likely rates of illness among the population and calculate rates by which insurers cover their costs and generate a reasonable profit. The basic concept is to spread risk across the population, thus allowing every individual to have affordable coverage.

Employers directly experience the concept of rating coverage when receiving their annual policy renewals. They must provide detailed demographics on employees and the employee must also identify their care histories, ages, and weight and smoking habits, which are all taken into account when the rating renewals are generated. The insurer's recent experience with the group is also considered. These all impact the prices for group renewal.

Think now of this process on a much larger scale, across large diverse populations. Insurers work within these bounds every day as they weigh their overall risk across the millions of lives they insure. Think now what the impact might be if you take the youngest and healthiest people out of this equation. The cost of coverage for the remaining population is likely to increase or even skyrocket as greater expenses are shared across a smaller population.

This is a potential dilemma that could face the industry in the post-tsunami days. The greatest challenge may be that there is little that can be done to stop it. The young and healthy will become educated, and when they do, they will find their best options. How will the rest of the system adjust?

Insurance is now and always has been a benefit. While the government seeks to provide proper care and treatment for all citizens in this country, that does not mean that all of us have equal benefits within the system. This is clear when we look at differences between the levels of coverage of the average citizen and groups like union or government employees. They often threaten to strike when asked to pay as little as $50 per month for their coverage. The average consumer is paying many times that and has a lower level of coverage for the investment they made.

Healthcare is not, in reality, a right under our current structure. Even the government system of care (Medicare and Medicaid) has clear limitations on consumer choice, usage, and the rates paid to providers. Even with these controls, costs continue to rise and the system is in danger of being bankrupt in our lifetime. The private health insurance system is based on an investment for a specific level of benefit. The more you spend, the more you get. We are now finding that consumers, whether employer or employee, are no longer willing to pay endless amounts to receive healthcare. Constraints are being placed and cost has become a significant driver of the marketplace for both insurance and care.

An environment has developed in the United States where changing the healthcare system has moved from being a business decision to being one of basic human rights. The longer we make the argument that we all have the right to healthcare, the longer the process of correcting the system will take. Whether by design or just sheer luck, healthcare is moving in a direction that has the potential to fix many of the key issues that have been driving the cost of care through the roof.

What is the secret? We just need to get everyone and everything out of the way of consumers and let this happen. After that, market forces will bring the system into balance, just as they have in virtually every other industry in the world. It may be more painful for some than for others, but that may be a necessary evil. Government's role should be to foster an environment of change that takes into consideration its commitment to those it provides care for, and those that may not be able to afford care. This can be done while allowing market forces to correct many of the problems of the healthcare industry. Doing this may help control both the size and the speed of the coming tsunami.

6 Providers as Producers

As we look at the healthcare industry, it is interesting to compare it to other industries and their evolution. This may provide some insight into the healthcare industry—how it has changed and how it might evolve in the future as the force of consumerism wash over it.

Most industries go through significant changes driven by consumer needs and the interaction of both direct and indirect players in the category. Let's take a common one: consumer products, which includes everything from toasters and blenders to more consumable products such as air fresheners and paper towels. If we go back in history to the 1920's, we will find that the period of the 1920's through the 1950's and even beyond was dominated by what many call a production mentality. Demand for products grew rapidly and often beyond the ability of manufacturers to meet the needs of the market. The focus of business was on production.

Companies needed to have the infrastructure and capacity to pump out these products. The goal was maximizing the capacity of current and future production facilities.

"FIRST, WE'RE GOING TO RUN SOME TESTS TO HELP PAY OFF THE MACHINE."

www.cartoonstock.com

As capacity and production capabilities came into balance with demand, the industry found that producers were no longer flooded with backlogs and were actually producing more than they were able to sell. They also found that they had built infrastructure that required high sales volumes to run cost effectively. This meant that they had to keep that capacity at near-full levels to be successful. This transition led to a new generation of thought called the sales mentality.

Aggressive sales and marketing techniques to get product placed in retail locations characterized this stage. While these activities today would not necessarily be called marketing, they were certainly the foundational components of those activities. The goal was simple: get your products into the distribution channel by whatever means possible. The goal was to sell as much product as capacity was able to produce.

This was a very push-driven environment from the perspective of the manufacturer. The sales mentality was to push products into the marketplace, and the general belief was that consumers would purchase whatever the manufacturer made available. Even consumer marketing and advertising had a definite sales tone to it. The needs of that consumer were not important; it was simply a matter of selling the product.

This general process began a shift in power in the consumer products industry. When production exceeds demand, cost becomes a key issue, as more products are competing for fewer dollars. The channel for consumer products was the retailer, and retailers came to learn that they carried more power as consumer product manufacturers sought to drive their products through the retail channel. Before long, retailers came to understand the degree and income potential of that power.

The sales mentality was relatively short-lived and led to the next generation in the process, the retail mentality. In this environment, the retailer drove much of the consumer product industry. Having a great product was only valuable if you could acquire premium shelf space for it, and have the retail partnering necessary to drive it to the market. Many good products failed because they were never offered to consumers in the mass market. Distribution was, and still is, essential to success, and retailers hold the keys.

A combination of retail control and consumer demand drives product success in today's marketplace. Manufacturers must be able to show a retailer that they have a good product, one that consumers want and will pay for. This generates interest from the retailer and initiates the negotiation for shelf space. The manufacturer demonstrates its product value through extensive product development and research work.

So how does this compare to healthcare? You may be surprised to find that there are many similarities even though the product is very different. Healthcare, while a service, is consumed in much the same way as other products. Like manufacturers, the providers of the product (medical care) have production facilities (clinics and hospitals). These facilities require extensive capital, much like manufacturing facilities.

Like manufacturers, clinics and hospitals are operated to maximize their efficiency and use. They have extensive staff and scheduling programs to get the greatest value for their resources. The key to efficiency is keeping people and equipment busy and doing work that generates revenue. While over scheduling can potentially upset the customer, keeping schedules full is an important component of success.

Since there is clear value to providers to keep the schedules, rooms, and technology in full use, and since the person

www.cartoonstock.com

who is the subject of these services is not the one paying for them, problems can arise. Industry leaders cite duplication of services as one of the issues contributing to the high cost of care. Duplicated tests, and over-utilization of both testing and services are some examples.

We have seen a rapid expansion of healthcare facilities in most U.S. markets. While the aging population has increased demand, most industry experts agree that we have more healthcare capacity than we need. Filling this capacity is essential to these organizations and their success. An exception to this is found in small markets and rural markets where providers are leaving to find more fertile ground to grow a practice.

Certainly there is no formal declaration of filling capacity as a goal in most healthcare organizations; it is clearly an unspoken truth. Most incentive systems—for everyone from line-level staff to physicians and specialists—are tied to volume. Generating higher volumes is to the personal benefit of the staff member. Until recently, physicians had no incentive to ensure proper utilization or eliminate duplication in testing or services. Some insurance companies have recognized this tendency and have instituted financial reward programs for facilities that effectively monitor utilization and streamline operations.

The current healthcare system has operated successfully under the production model for years. The healthcare industry is advancing so quickly that its next likely stage is that of the market-driven provider system. Under this system, quality, costs, and value will drive the market. Providers will have to find new ways to operate that reward team members for things like efficiency, customer service, and cost savings. They may also reward staff for finding new products and services that meet consumer needs.

We believe the production model in healthcare can no longer function after the tsunami. Downward pressure on price and a lack of volume may even force some providers to go out of business. In markets where total demand is not sufficient to support multiple networks, those that can meet the needs of consumers and their wallets will be successful. We also anticipate an emerging surge of specialization, where niche markets emerge and compete in specific diagnostic and delivery areas. Convenience, cost, and customer service will play major roles in a post-tsunami marketplace.

7 The Pharmaceutical Catch-22

New medical devices and medications have saved millions of lives in the past 20 years alone. Advancements range from new heart medications and devices to tools that improve the quality of life for those with diabetes or acid reflux. Add to these major innovations in treatment techniques and exciting breakthroughs on the horizon in the areas of cancer, spinal cord injuries, and AIDS. Few major maladies have not benefited from a wave of innovation in healthcare.

Much has been written about the impact of skyrocketing prescription medicine costs and cutting-edge medical device costs on the growth in healthcare spending. New medications and tools are usually based on patents that give a single company exclusive rights to the product and its pricing. This is clearly a factor that will play an important role in future costs as well.

"THIS SECOND PRESCRIPTION IS TO CALM YOU DOWN AFTER YOU SEE THE COST OF THE FIRST ONE."

www.cartoonstock.com

But the general public may not know or fully understand an interesting aspect of this story. It is true that the current healthcare system has generated significantly rising costs. But at the same time, it has also provided some of the most significant medical and pharmaceutical innovations in the history of mankind, made possible by an environment that encourages enormous investments in research and development projects.

Not every drug or product innovation actually makes it to the marketplace. Many are deemed failures somewhere during development. Some generate unacceptable levels of complications that make the product a medical risk or otherwise unacceptable to physicians and their patients. All of these products, regardless of whether they ever reach the market to generate revenue, require an investment of millions in time and human resources to reach the testing point. Somewhere, manufacturers must recover their research and development costs and often do so with the successful launch of a new product. The dollars raised in that launch must offset losses from products that did not make it to the marketplace.

As we look at large medical device and pharmaceutical companies, we must understand that they are not only driven by profit and product, but also driven to increase the valuation of their stock. Public companies today are led by a professional board of directors constantly striving to generate a sound return for the investors and stockholders. As a result, many of top management's incentives and compensation methods are tied to stock and stock options. Human nature then causes top company leadership to constantly review activities in light of their potential impact on stock value and price.

We have all witnessed a company see a serious short-term decline in its stock prices when a new medication or device fails in clinical trials, or receives negative press about its release or use. Companies' valuations can drop by millions of dollars in a single day because of these issues. Significant potential for return requires significant risk and, over the long haul, success is based on finding a winner.

The third-party-payer arrangement in healthcare allows pharmaceutical and device manufacturing companies significant latitude in pricing and use of their products. Since the user of the product, the patient, is not paying for it, the companies can set higher prices. This makes the investment in product development more attractive, and more investments are made. Many of these innovations and medications are priced dramatically differently outside the United States. In order to sell products in socialized markets such as Canada, pharmaceutical companies have to drop the price. They simply can't achieve their sales margins in that environment.

Some of these innovations might never have made it to market under a true consumer model. A true consumer model might require a longer introductory period as consumers decide whether they will spend their dollars on new products and treatments. This increases costs and slows the rate of return on the investments.

So what will the future bring? The world will always need medical innovation and progress to continue lengthening the human life span and increasing the quality of life for millions of people who will now live well into their 80s and beyond. The question is how these continued advances will be funded. Will consumerism be able to control large companies seeking to generate significant returns on large investments of time and money? Will it create two classes of healthcare—one class for those who can afford the latest tools and medication and another for those who have to live within specific budgets? Only time will tell.

In the meantime, pharmaceutical companies and medical device manufacturers make significant investments in lobbying, and will likely continue to work toward acquiring the benefits of patent rights and minimal control of pricing. Legislation may favor a slower reform of the system to give companies the opportunity to recoup investments made over the past 10 years.

Many new tools and technologies are focusing on a consumer-driven model and a more consumer-based environment. These tools allow patients to leave the hospital sooner and be monitored at home through remote technology via phone or Internet connection. These new tools will put continued downward pressure on costs and help free up healthcare dollars for other purposes.

Most consumers would agree that they seek to have the best-quality medical care available. It is likely that regardless of the changes in the marketplace, U.S. companies will continue to lead the way in technology development. Whether the new economic model will change the way these products are developed and how they are introduced into the new landscape created by the tsunami becomes the question. The impending change is likely being discussed in boardrooms across the country and is already generating a change in the development process.

Pharmaceutical producers may have already tested the water for this new delivery model. Twenty years ago, the marketing of a new drug was a relatively simple process. A drug was introduced to physicians and they were educated on its benefits and use. Companies worked to generate prescriptions from physicians through a variety of marketing programs. Ultimately, physicians drove the success of a new medication.

Drug makers now recognize the benefits of marketing their medications through multiple channels. This continues to include physicians, who are a vital resource for both the manufacturer and the patient. They also market through other healthcare professionals such as physician assistants (PAs) and nurse practitioners (NPs). Some even market through nursing and office staff trying to generate positive discussion about their product in an office environment. In the marketing industry this is called "push marketing," which is a process that is sales oriented.

The newest activities involve what is known in marketing circles as "pull marketing," designed to create consumer demand for a product and pull that demand through the distribution channel. Drug companies create demand through consumer advertising on a variety of levels. Whether it's newspapers, magazines, radio, television, or websites, the volume of drug marketing and advertising has been staggering in recent years. This is all designed to get consumers to go to their doctor and request, or at least discuss, specific medications for their condition. Consumer influence has changed the face of drug marketing forever and puts at least that part of the industry on a better track for life after the tsunami.

Drug companies view advertising as an investment in their product. As with all investments, they expect a return. The current level of advertising is fueled, in part, by the drug maker's ability to price its product in a way that will allow it to recoup its investment in marketing and advertising. This may be more challenging when consumers are paying for the product directly.

However, the reality is that whether the drug is being paid for by the employer, the insurer, or the consumer directly, we may always be looking for that next miracle. We will always desire the drug that will cure obesity and allow us to lose weight without making personal sacrifices, or the medical device that will save our life after a cardiac episode, and the cure for debilitating conditions such as diabetes, multiple sclerosis, or cancer. These represent major steps in the advancement of medical technology that will not only improve the quality of life for millions, but save lives. While we hate to even discuss putting a price on these treatments, we may have to in the future. That price may turn out to be more than some consumers can afford. Will this create a two-tiered health system with only the wealthy and those on government coverage able to afford treatment? Perhaps.

We must also remember that the industries that represent these products are not going to go quietly into the night as consumerism puts downward pressure on their pricing and marketing practices. The medical manufacturing and pharmaceutical industries already spend millions of dollars annually on lobbying to protect their environment and their margins. They may work to slow the consumerism process or attempt to direct it in a way that allows them greater flexibility in the future.

Some industry insiders believe there will be little to no short-term impact from consumerism in the marketplace. Most of these products take 10 years or more to bring to the marketplace successfully. Items that we will see in the next 5 to 7 years have likely been in development for 5 years or more. The patent process also gives the manufacturer a period of about 17 years to protect its development and take advantage of its innovation in the market. Therefore, little change may be possible or realistic for 20 years or more. Alternative methods to address the costs related to product advancement in the consumer marketplace may need to be developed.

Consumers will still have significant influence on these industries, regardless of this protectionism. Consumers will select tools and technologies that best meet their needs and, perhaps more importantly, their budgets. While physicians will continue to play a significant role in determining the tools used, they too will be questioned by more savvy consumers as to the true value of these tools and their return on investment for dollars spent.

We believe that direct marketing to consumers of drugs and some medical devices and technologies will become increasingly common. Innovators will take their case to the people and attempt to demonstrate the value they offer consumers, not only in terms of the physical quality of their lives, but also in terms of their financial quality of life. They will need to back this up with sound information and education.

8 Government's Dual Role

The government plays an interesting dual role in the healthcare industry and thus will play a significant role in its future. While the government, on many levels, monitors and often regulates the healthcare industry, it is also the industry's largest single customer. Medicare and Medicaid represent the health coverage of approximately 80 million Americans—a quarter of the lives in the United States. This gives the government the distinction of having the most at stake in changing the healthcare system.

Medicare and Medicaid are relatively new to America. Enacted by President Lyndon B. Johnson in 1965, Medicare was added to the Social Security Act to extend healthcare coverage to all Americans over the age of 65. The act also provided coverage for those living in poverty, especially children, who may not have access to healthcare because of financial limitations. The goal was to give long-term health to a nation in need. Former president Harry Truman was present at the signing and credited with creating the foundation for modern health insurance in the United States.

Deeper roots can be found for Medicaid, which dates back to 1950, when the first federal payments were authorized in public assistance amendments. The goal was to match state funds already being paid to a select group of vendors who were providing care to those receiving state welfare benefits. Medicaid now represents coverage for 54 million Americans and has a budget of more than $320 million (2005) when looking at the combination of state and federal funding.

In 1960, the Kerr-Mills Act introduced a new and relatively simple program designed to create a semiautomatic matching formula for state and federal funds. It had no global cap and was tied to the per capita income of individual states, a move seen as fair to both rich and poor states. One of its more important features was coverage for the medically indigent—specifically, individuals over age 65 who were not receiving old-age assistance cash. This would be the foundation of the 1965 Medicare program, but it also relegated coverage for those under 65 to the welfare system.

Medicaid plans are run by individual states and can vary in their level of coverage due to their ties to welfare, which can also vary significantly by state. While the 1965 act required some standardization of coverage to meet federal matching requirements, it still gave the states significant latitude.

Currently, Medicare and Medicaid programs represent 1 in 4 people using health services, and 1 in 3 dollars spent on healthcare, up from only 1 in 10 dollars spent as recently as the 1970s. In 2006, a prescription drug program was added and instantly made the government one of the largest consumers of medications as well. Government's expenditures on healthcare are in the billions of dollars, and just like employers, it is seeking to find a way to ease the pain and financial liability of continuing to provide coverage.

The Medicare system shows strong user satisfaction—higher satisfaction rates than those of individuals who are covered by other commercial programs. The Healthcare Finance Review cites data indicating that 68% of Medicare beneficiaries rate their coverage as excellent or very good as compared to 44% for commercial insurance users. Medicare users also have stronger perceptions of receiving the best medical care available when they need it. This is clearly an example of a government program that is working and meeting the needs of citizens. Studies indicate that Medicare patients are indicating greater access to care when needed and are less likely than those on commercial coverage to delay care due to cost concerns.

While the Medicare system clearly faces financial challenges due to the increasing population of baby boomers moving into the system, there is no evidence that their expenditures are any different than those of the rest of the market. In fact, some studies indicate that Medicare expenditures have increased in recent years at a rate that is slightly slower than their commercial counterparts.

As the baby boomer population moves through the Medicare system, something will need to change. Calls will be made to force beneficiaries to take on a greater portion of payment for their care, just as the rest of the industry is being forced to do. That is already going on to a certain extent, as a Maxwell, Storeygard, and Moon 2002 study indicated that only 58% of medical costs are actually covered by Medicare.

Requiring seniors to pay more of their care is somewhat problematic. The Employee Benefits Institute estimates that people age 65 today will require $100,000 to cover their out-of-pocket expenses through the balance of their lives. If they live to age 95, that number jumps to a whopping $340,000. This means that as the miracles of modern healthcare extend our life expectancy, we can count on an average couple easily needing $500,000 to cover their healthcare costs. Many seniors today do not have those resources, which dramatically restricts the ability of Medicare to force patients to share more of the cost of care.

A variety of new strategies are being considered to address these issues, one of which would create a new tool called Medicare Health Accounts. These would be funded by automatic wage contributions to personal accounts to cover out-of-pocket and premium costs related to care during the Medicare years. They could also be used to fund long-term care needs, which are expected to increase dramatically in coming years. A Commonwealth Fund survey of older adults age 50 to 70 indicates that they are receptive to this concept, and the results were consistent across geographic, income, and political lines.

The concept would call for working-age adults to deposit 1% of their wages into these accounts, which would be invested in government securities.

Centers for Medicare & Medicaid Services (CMS), the federal agency created to fund and manage Medicare and Medicaid, has taken major steps in the past decade to improve the quality of care provided and control future costs. It has explored alternative payment and reimbursement models and mandated quality measurement with the potential of tying quality to reimbursement. CMS is also creating demonstration models that share cost savings with providers and health plans if quality and outcomes are maintained.

Marshfield Clinic, a Wisconsin private practice clinic with more than 750 physicians and specialists, recently demonstrated that providers could impact both the long-term health and costs of caring for patients with chronic conditions. A July 13, 2007, article in the *New York Times* noted the study that ran for three years from 2005 to 2007 as an attempt to rethink the way in which the government reimburses doctors. Ten physician groups were part of this particular study.

The study indicates a potential to reduce hospital utilization and overall costs by better managing the care received for chronic conditions such as diabetes and heart conditions. All 10 groups showed improvement in the first year of the study, yet only 2 of these groups hit specific targets to generate payment bonuses, one of which was Marshfield Clinic. These two providers received a bonus of $7.3 million dollars for saving

Medicare $9.5 million dollars. Participants believe they saved the Medicare system a total of $21 million dollars during the first three years of the experiment, and this does not include the long-term benefit of the changes made.

The study shows that increased communication with patients after key healthcare contacts helps in increasing compliance with instructions, follow-up care, and needed medications. Both physician and nursing staff provided this communication through a variety of formats, including telephone follow-up with patients. Marshfield Clinic has not only implemented the identified changes with its CMS population, but has done so across its entire system, saving employers and consumers millions of dollars in the process. These programs demonstrate that even high-cost items such as chronic conditions and care can be improved and better managed to the benefit of the patient and those paying for the services.

Some experts are calling for the development of some level of consumerism even in the Medicare program. Studies like those cited above are designed to maximize the efficiency of care delivery systems in America. However, maximizing efficiency addresses only part of the problem, as there would then be a need to get Medicare patients to these high-performance providers. Discussion is taking place about creating financial incentives to use high-performance networks and providers by waiving the Medicare cost-sharing requirements when using these outlets.

The aging of America continues as the baby boomers move toward retirement. So, the government's role as the major customer of healthcare is much the same as that of the employer. It is providing coverage while it has little or no control over how consumers use the services. Thus, it shares the problem that any employer has, which is determining how to get the actual users of services to do so wisely and efficiently. Long-term solutions are needed to protect this important system in the future.

Clearly, the future of Medicare is not bright. Studies indicate that the system could be bankrupt by 2030 as rising costs and increasing population size put pressure on the system's resources. Costs are already projected to double between now and 2015. Not enough people are paying into the system to cover the cost increases generated by baby boomers moving through the system. Government must take action now to ensure the solvency of this important system.

Another major government activity in healthcare was the passage of the Health Insurance Portability and Accountability Act (HIPAA). The movement toward legislation started innocently enough in 1975 when a group of healthcare providers and payers joined together to discuss the creation of a standard hospital claims form. This would lead to the adoption of the UB-82 form, which was used by 60% of hospitals as of 1988.

Twenty-one years later, in 1996, this form led to the enactment of HIPAA, which mandates administrative simplification procedures. While these administrative codes were only a small part of the total legislation that was primarily designed to give American workers portability in their health insurance, the codes would have a profound effect on everybody they touched.

The HIPAA legislation is actually an IRS code and is also known as the Kennedy-Kassebaum Act. It called upon the Health and Human Services administration to do three things:

1. Standardize electronic patient health and financial data.
2. Generate unique identifiers for individuals, employers, health plans, and providers.
3. Create security standards to protect the confidentiality of individually identifiable health information.

The act prompted sweeping changes in the way in which healthcare information is handled in both administrative and financial environments, touching anyone who might have contact with patient information. Civil penalties of $25,000 to

$250,000 and criminal penalties of up to 10 years in prison can result from violations and noncompliance.

Even in 2007, providers are scrambling to meet deadlines associated with standardized transactions and the protection of patient privacy, as well as electronic claims processing and government data collection. New HIPAA rules are pending that will outline further requirements for anyone who touches patient information.

The goal of protecting patient privacy was a sound one, especially in today's society where identity theft is common. Providers, however, felt that the plan could hamper patient care by requiring a significant sign-off process by patients prior to receiving care. The rule was eventually modified in 2002 when President Bush dropped the requirement that patients consent to the use of their information in care and treatment environments.

HIPAA will continue to have a dramatic impact on healthcare providers, as it requires a significant system to be in compliance with all of the rules for the collection, handling, and use of data obtained during the process of care. This certainly has an impact not only on the operations of healthcare systems, but also on the administrative costs related to everything from information management to claims processing.

Government's legislative and regulatory activities have a major impact on the healthcare industry and also on its future. Government can lead by either dangling a carrot or prodding with a stick. Evidence shows that both may be needed in order to meet timelines that are already close at hand. The crisis could occur in the next 10 years, and the changes needed are in a gigantic industry not accustomed to change. The right tools will be essential in meeting the goals of change.

Because of the significant dollars at play, the healthcare industry as a whole has major involvement in lobbying activities and seeks to have input into the future of healthcare regulation. A review of the lobbying database from *opensecrets.org* shows that the Medical Device Manufacturers Association alone almost tripled its lobbying investments between 2005 and 2006, to $550,000. The association is not alone in its investment to sway legislators in decisions related to the healthcare industry.

The pharmaceutical and health products industry shows annual contributions of $19 million in 2006, with a growing portion coming from political action committees (PACs). This industry may feel that PACs are generating better results for it than would making individual or targeted contributions. These donations are seen as investments made to ensure a proper legislative environment for the growth of the industry and its members' businesses.

The same source shows that health professionals as a group contributed a total of just under $54 million to political candidates, with $21 million of that coming from PACs. Twenty million dollars went to the Democrats and $33 million to Republicans, ranking them as number six. Spending was actually down from $74 million during the 2004 presidential elections.

Overall, the health segment contributed $98 million in 2006, once again down from $123 million during the 2004 elections. In recent years, funds given to Republican candidates have increased more dramatically than those given to their Democratic counterparts. This may be a factor of the parties' positions on issues and their control of key committees.

Well over $100 million is spent annually to lobby our political system with regard to healthcare issues. This creates an interesting scenario in which the largest single customer of healthcare is being persuaded to take positions on issues that may actually negatively impact its position as a consumer.

As noted earlier, plans abound on the political landscape, at both the state and federal levels, for programs that will generate change and solve the healthcare crisis. Massachusetts is one state considered to be on the leading edge of reform. It was the first to successfully enact a universal coverage plan that brought together existing funds and programs in the state with a modest new tax on business. Massachusetts has been cited as an example for other states in the nation, such as California and Wisconsin, that are looking at their own versions of full coverage for their citizens.

A July 25, 2007, article in the *Wall Street Journal* states that while the Massachusetts plan strives to cover the 550,000 uninsured in the state, simply providing insurance does not make a successful program. The state is suffering from a significant physician shortage. Three teaching hospitals in Boston indicate that 95% of their general practice physicians have stopped accepting patients. Part of the issue appears to be reimbursement rates, which are comparable to Medicare reimbursement rates under the plan.

Universal plans must take into consideration whether their delivery systems are equipped to handle the uninsured and whether the financial equation gives physicians a reason to provide care. Government will clearly play a key role in the coming tsunami, but it is not always clear whether it will be an innovator or a roadblock.

9 Financial Services Position Themselves to Ride the Wave

What does banking have to do with healthcare? Why would the financial services industry be positioning itself to be a player in the future of the healthcare industry? The answer is actually quite simple. Billions of dollars have already changed hands and will continue to shift with the growth of HSAs. Since money is their business, banks and credit unions are vying for their share of the financial power.

The coming tsunami will significantly change the financial landscape of healthcare. This change will be generated by a shift in who has the money and where it is kept. The consumer holding more of his or her own investment in healthcare will form the foundation of this new financial landscape. Those who have held this money, insurers and providers, will hold less of it. Where this money is housed and how it will be used will affect the investment of billions of future dollars.

The signs of change began subtly, as changes in banking regulations gave banks the ability to offer insurance products as part of their financial offerings. While this began with products such as life insurance, which have financial ramifications, the industry began to offer full lines of insurance products, including health coverage. Agents and brokers employed by banks now offer health products and related consulting services.

Medical savings accounts (MSAs), the initial move at consumerism, also sparked interest from the financial industry. These predecessors to HSAs and health reimbursement accounts (HRAs) had many of the same features, including the consumer holding a special savings account for medical funding. Banks sought to establish MSAs and offer a new financial tool to consumers. MSAs were limited to the self-employed or small businesses employing fewer than 50 employees, but they set the stage for HSAs that are much more inclusive.

Many firms that service the financial services industry also got involved. One example is Fiserv, a provider of information management systems and services to the financial, insurance, and health benefit industries, based in Milwaukee, Wisconsin. Fiserv provides services to banks, credit unions, lending institutions, and investment advisors; insurance companies and agents; and health plan administration. It first began acquiring companies related to insurance, investment, and brokerage services in order to create seamless solutions for banking and credit union clients. As it became clear that health benefits would also be a part of the future of the financial services industry, Fiserv began purchasing companies that provided software and data solutions to employers and healthcare clients.

Fiserv occupies a unique position, in that it brings together a strong understanding of the financial industry and strong tools for data management and use. Fiserv has grown by acquisition and numbers more than 140 companies. The Fiserv Health subsidiary, which was recently purchased by UnitedHealth Group, is made up of companies that provide services to assist in health plan administration, claims processing, care management, consumer education, pharmacy benefits management, and more. These services are integrated to provide clients single-source access.

Fiserv Health, prior to its purchase by UnitedHealth Group, brought to its clients a consumerism strategy that started with building ownership in the concept of HSAs and demonstrated their value in promoting both health and wealth. The company then partnered with clients to both inform and educate them about key issues of consumerism, wellness, and prevention. The final step in its approach was to engage participants and take steps that encouraged positive actions. A full line of integrated live, printed, and online tools supported this effort, making it easy for the employer, insurer, or consumer to use the services. It is unclear if or how the purchase by UnitedHealth Group will change the way the company has structured its business process.

Now, many players who had been in banking services are integrating healthcare and insurance into their offerings. Healthcare consultants and service providers are also expanding their customer base by offering services to the banking industry, helping these new entrants understand the healthcare industry and its needs.

The coming tsunami will move dollars that used to be held by the health insurance industry into the hands of consumers and, in theory, into their HSAs. The term *health savings account* inherently references financial matters and, thus, banking. The insurance industry decided it would not take this change lying down. It determined that if banking was going to get involved in insurance, it was only fair that insurance get involved in banking.

While some life insurance and annuity providers began offering savings, checking, and investment accounts many years ago, it is only in the past year that we have seen major players in the health insurance industry seek and be granted bank charters. Two recent charters worth noting were granted to UnitedHealth Group (Exante), of Minneapolis, and the national Blue Cross Blue Shield Association (Blue Bank), one of the originators of group health plans in the United States.

When Blue Cross Blue Shield needed a banking platform to support its newly founded financial institution, it turned to Fiserv, which gave it the infrastructure and software for item processing and other basic transactions. This is a great example of how the once clear lines between industries are blurring, and how financial services and health coverage are coming together to form a new model that will offer the consumer seamless solutions.

Both Blue Cross Blue Shield and UnitedHealth Group now offer HSAs to their customers as part of their total package of offerings. Will other investment and financial products be far behind? Will we see these two powerful industries move closer together? And will the integration create new opportunities for both employers and consumers?

The financial industry initially showed little interest in offering HSAs as part of its standard line of services. This was based on the fact it viewed these as transaction accounts like checking accounts. Checking accounts are not profitable accounts for financial institutions and are offered primarily to build relationships with customers.

HSAs are relatively new and lack history. Banks assumed that consumers would make frequent transactions from these accounts based upon the purpose of the account and because many incorporated a checkbook component. After the first few years, however, research indicated that as many as 60% of account holders never touched their accounts during any given year. This is logical, as many of these account holders are young and healthy. It is also logical when considering the fact that 85% of consumers spend less than $500 per year on health services.

With this base of knowledge, banks saw that these accounts were really investment accounts, which is an attractive product for most financial institutions. The accounts are likely to grow over time, and, along with this growth, clients will need additional services such as investment accounts and financial planning services. Most financial institutions are now offering HSAs or are planning to do so in the near future. This will advance the product line as institutions compete for consumer accounts and find better tools and offerings to make them attractive.

Another aspect of consumerism that the financial industry views as having potential is a growing new field called health

"Doctor Wilson believes in preventive financing, so regardless of your insurance, fill out this loan application form."

www.cartoonstock.com

finance. Both traditional banks and consumer credit organizations see the opportunity to provide short-term funding to cover medical needs, ranging from gap coverage to funding elective procedures such as cosmetic surgery, which may not be covered under traditional insurance coverage.

The financing of care is even impacting the marketing of services. Some providers of laser eye procedures or high-end cosmetic dental procedures offer free short-term financing, allowing consumers to fund them the same as they do automotive and home electronics purchases. These financing options will likely have a positive impact on sales in healthcare just as they do in other situations.

CapitalOne, Citigroup, and CareCredit (a unit of GE) are already major players in this new category. This is an attractive area, as studies indicate that many consumers are covering these costs currently using credit cards, often at interest rates of 15% to 22%. Consumer credit models offering interest rates of 12% to 15% are often a better alternative. Traditional financial institutions also see the opportunity to offer consumer line-of-credit services that cover gaps in healthcare costs on either a short- or long-term basis.

Industry players indicate a need for such funding alternatives due to the fact that HSAs are still in their infancy. A study by *Inside Consumer-Directed Care*, a trade publication, indicates the average balance in these accounts to be just over $1,300. This often means they have a shortfall in early years. The Exante Bank unit of UnitedHealth Group is testing a card that extends credit to its account holders at interest rates of between 10% and 13% based on credit history. It will ultimately be the consumer who determines whether these offerings are valuable.

Financial institutions have a lot to gain under the new consumerism that will be created by the coming tsunami. They see a significant shift in wealth occurring and are a natural beneficiary of the shift. Consumers are accustomed to working with financial institutions and trust them for financial services and advice. Financial institutions have a clear advantage over other players who are now starting to offer HSAs and do not have the same history or financial experience. It is logical to assume that banks are the likely front-runners for these new accounts, and other players will have to offer unique tools and programs to break the existing relationships. Competition is always healthy and helps to bring better products and services to the consumer.

10 Employers Reach Their Limit

To this point, we have discussed a number of players and industries that have impacted the healthcare industry and have contributed to the coming tsunami. The size of the wave and the speed at which it is released will be determined in large part by employers. Employers will play a pivotal role in the coming wave of change, as they have provided the bulk of healthcare coverage outside that provided by the government.

As outlined in Chapter 3, employer-provided coverage in America has grown from a tool to differentiate employers during wage freezes to a major benefit that has become a perceived entitlement. The issue of health coverage has prompted national strikes and even closed some businesses due to rising costs and the need to compete in the world market. With costs escalating by double digits annually, employer-provided coverage has reached a critical point.

"Yes, we do have health benefits, but read the fine print. You're only allowed to get sick once every three years."

Two types of coverage exist within the employer ranks: self-insurance and commercial insurance. Larger employers have become self-insured, which means that they have established funds, much like HSAs, used to pay for the care of their employees. They balance this with the use of a risk management tool called stop-loss insurance. Stop-loss insurance covers the costs related to care of either high-cost individual claims or aggregate claims. These plans have the same incentive as HSAs in that funds that are not spent build for future use. Thus, you can see why employers have an active interest in the health of their employees.

Smaller employers generally offer some type of commercial coverage. This coverage is provided through a variety of national and regional players. The employee determines the level of risk he or she will accept by the selection of both deductibles and the overall plan design. These plans today are most commonly tapping HMOs or PPOs, which require the use of specific provider networks for compensation. HMOs and PPOs negotiate with provider networks to secure the best possible rates for services used. Most commercial insurance is subject to annual renewal and rating.

Employers have been unable to budget for and fund rising healthcare costs. This is true both for large employers who are self-insured and for small employers using commercial coverage. Employers have come to realize that they have little control or influence over the way their employees use healthcare services. Our recent surveys reveal that employers believe employees do not understand their coverage or how to use it. They also believe that employees are not good partners in the control of either current or future healthcare costs. They feel that employees do not understand the product and, thus, cannot be good consumers of services.

Many attempts have been made by employers to control their current and future healthcare costs. Some use occupational health programs from providers and outside consulting firms to manage the process of caring for sick or injured employees. The goal of these programs is not only to control the cost of the actual care and treatment of the employee, but also to reduce lost productivity. These programs constitute a critical contact point between healthcare providers and employers.

Another significant cost to employers is dealing with chronic conditions. Studies indicate that chronic illnesses can double the number of office visits, as well as the costs related to ongoing monitoring, care, and treatment. Providers and outside consultants offer case management services to create care plans for controlling both short- and long-term costs while maintaining the health and productivity of the employee.

Prevention and wellness programs have been around for more than 20 years to educate employees about taking better care of their bodies. A healthier employee will cost less to insure today and in the future. He or she will also be more productive and generate less downtime. Some studies indicate that 50% to 70% of healthcare costs are a direct result of lifestyle choices made by the patient. This is an important issue for employers and is fast becoming one for consumers.

Many of these programs go beyond simple education and offer incentives for healthy behaviors, ranging from memberships at health clubs to cash incentives or reduced premiums. Some even offer personal health coaches designed to keep employees on track and achieving their goals. These are generally offered through both online programs and telephone-based programs in which health coaches have live discussions with program participants. The goal is to increase compliance and give support to positive lifestyle changes.

Unfortunately, too many companies do not see an immediate return on their investment in wellness and consider it an unnecessary expense. Many feel that wellness is their employees' responsibility. They believe that those who take advantage of these programs are generally those who were showing healthy behaviors already. Therefore, they are not meeting their goal of improving employee health and generating reductions in future risk.

Managed care was also a tool designed to help employers and large groups manage the process of care delivery. The goal was to create a set of structured gatekeepers that would help the employee navigate the healthcare system properly. Gatekeepers would ensure that expensive specialty care was controlled and only used when deemed medically appropriate. The use of testing and procedures would be closely monitored and require preapproval based on a specific set of parameters established in complicated care management models. While this was the primary tool for controlling costs for almost 15 years, managed care plan designs have fallen out of favor with employers because of their cumbersome approval systems and lack of financial return. In addition, employees find many of the processes confusing and time-consuming.

Employers have banded together to form business coalitions. The goal of these coalitions is to bring together the mass purchasing strength of large and mid-sized employers. They leverage their purchasing power to negotiate the best rates with providers and third-party administrators who manage the claims of their employees and administer their health plans. They also offer shared education programs, prevention screenings, and more.

All of these efforts were sincere and valid attempts to control cost, which is seemingly out of the employers' control. None of these measures have proven to be totally effective in achieving the ultimate goal of keeping employees healthy and costs within a manageable and budgetable range. After years of hard work with little reward, employers have reached the end of their rope.

In both qualitative and quantitative work completed by The Leede Research Group in the past two years, we have seen clear evidence of the frustration employers feel regarding

www.cartoonstock.com

health coverage. Many employers have given up trying to find new tools and have resigned themselves to spending their budgeted healthcare dollars in the most efficient way possible, without causing significant employee complaints. They will migrate to the least expensive care options to address a continued need.

Our research with employers is showing an interesting pattern. Employers now believe that there is very little difference between the providers of either insurance or healthcare in terms of quality. This is leading to a commodity mentality in which employers simply seek the best price, as they do not believe there are any significant advantages offered by any of the different players. This mentality is already seen in other areas of insurance such as property and casualty. In this environment, the brokers and consultants generally shop for the best package and bring it to the employers. Employers will rely on their relationships with these brokers and consultants to bring them the best value.

In the past five to seven years, employers have started addressing this problem from another perspective. They have begun to quietly shift the burden of cost to their employees to gain incremental savings on premiums. Some of this has been done directly by sharing the cost of increased premiums with employees, yet much has been done far more subtly through changes in plan design.

Shifting out-of-pocket costs and deductible limits can allow employers to shift costs while not generating an immediate or noted response from their employees. Part of the reason for this is that the employees, or consumers, have never really taken the time to understand the way their coverage works. They simply used the services paid for by someone else. This lack of knowledge and understanding has allowed employers to shift the burden to employees in a manner that has often gone unnoticed, especially by younger employees who may not be frequent users of services.

Some small and mid-size employers shifted costs as long as they could and then simply got out of the business of health coverage. The Leede Research Group's work has found that in some regions where there are not significant numbers of large employers, the rate of employer-sponsored coverage has dropped to just over 50%. This has been driven not only by costs, but also by legislative changes. HIPAA legislation placed limits on the type of coverage that could be offered by employers. This made some employer plan options less competitive with choices available to young, healthy employees on their own. They soon migrated to private coverage and their employers stopped offering coverage. For example, plans cannot waive maternity care, even if employees indicate that they do not need or want such coverage. These rules often make the employer-sponsored plans more expensive and less competitive with plans employees can access on their own.

The Leede Research Group has conducted research studies with employers since the late 1980s. We have seen the level of frustration rise with costs. We have seen new tools become old and old tools become obsolete, as employers have been unable to stop the progression of costs regardless of what they invest. They have also transferred as much of the indirect costs possible under the existing coverage tools and models. They needed a new tool to help them create an environment in which they could continue the process of reducing their burden of costs for health coverage.

Enter the consumer-directed health plan (CDHP). This is a relatively new concept that has caught on rapidly in the employer community. Under these CDHPs, a high-deductible health plan is generally paired with another tool such as an HSA or HRA. The gap left between these two would generally equal the amount the employee normally would have paid in out-of-pocket costs under a traditional plan.

A recent study by The Leede Research Group for Fiserv Health (now part of UnitedHealth Group) looked at the activities of Fortune 1000 companies. This study found that while only 13% of these company's employees are currently covered under CDHPs, the five-year projection showed a mean of 48%. In the large-employer environment, these plans are developed within the companies' self-insured environment. This rapid growth is likely to change the face of both insurance and healthcare delivery as more employees are forced to be responsible for their own healthcare spending and related decisions. We believe that this will be a key factor in both the size and the speed of the coming tsunami.

A 2005 study by Forrester Research indicated that 2005 CDHP premiums were estimated at $16 billion, up from $3 billion in 2003. Forrester projects that premiums will reach $88 billion by 2007 and could exceed $400 billion by 2010. This would represent a 500% increase in just a three-year period! The study indicates that this growth is coming at the expense of traditional PPO and HMO plans. It is clear that employers are seeing CDHPs as their most viable solution at the current time.

As employers continue to make the shift to CDHPs they are forcing employees into a consumer environment. They are telling employees that they must be smarter and make better decisions if they are going to be financially successful under these plans. This process of change has caught most employees somewhat off guard. While they have heard employers' claims of rising costs for years, most employers never really did anything about it. Instead, employees saw modest changes in their coverage and premiums, but most went unnoticed.

The world of healthcare is now changing for employees. They are thrust into a new environment where they are starting to understand not only the impact of cost on the care they receive, but also how that cost can influence their financial future. Employees have moved from being the recipients of a gift from their employer to being true consumers of healthcare services. In this process, they may eventually become the partner that the employer has been seeking for the past 10 years: a partner that works with them to make better health decisions and controls costs.

Employers may finally see some light at the end of the tunnel at a time when they no longer care. The frustration level has been such that they have lost interest in working to control the future and are simply looking for convenient solutions for the present. It will be interesting to see whether the tsunami will raise employers' interest to a point where they return to a true partnership. This could increase both the size and speed of the tsunami and its ultimate impact.

11 Confused Consumers

We as consumers are starting to take responsibility for our healthcare spending. The problem is that we are not very good at it. We have never been particularly good at it. We have never had a reason to become good at it because we were generally not paying for it. While our employers and insurance companies have tried for years to educate and motivate us to make us better consumers, we have not shown much interest. In fact, we aren't all that sharp with even the basic terminology of our coverage and insurance.

In work that The Leede Research Group has done in the health industry for over 20 years, a consistent finding in studies ranging from providers to insurers to business coalitions has shown that we as consumers really do not know much about the coverage we have. We find that well over a third of consumers are not able to tell us what type of plan design they have. Those who do are often incorrect, based on comparisons of consumer survey results with actual market makeup.

As consumers, we really do not understand why we are paying more out of our own pockets than we used to. We really didn't listen when our employers indicated that they were changing the design of our health plan. We understood that the changes were being made to help control costs. While deductibles and out-of-pocket costs increased, we often did not notice it unless we happened to use services more heavily that year. We simply looked at what the premium was costing us every month. We understood that our share of the premium cost was going up, but it was a modest increase and was affordable. The design of our plan was never important because we were not paying for it and it really did not impact our behavior significantly. It seems like these days are now over.

We have never had to be good consumers of health services. The services generally cost us very little and were paid easily by presenting our insurance card at the desk. This "magic card" took care of everything, and the most challenging task we had was trying to understand the billing statements from providers. In many cases, even though we did not understand the bill, we let it go unpaid until someone contacted us or sent a second bill. Sometimes we paid things that we did not need to and then found refund checks in our mail months later. The whole system was little more than a confusing nuisance.

"I think what we'll do is rub some insurance money on it and see what happens."

We very seldom questioned the healthcare system about anything. We built a relationship with a physician. Most of us have had this relationship for 10 years or more. We rely on that physician to be our guide through the healthcare process. We trust that our physicians know what they are doing and access the tools that are needed for our care. We did not question why a test was needed, why name-brand medications were prescribed, or how much a procedure would cost before it was conducted. Since we were not paying for the work, we placed our trust in the professionals and assumed a quality outcome would result.

We now find ourselves in uncharted territory. We are paying for more of our own care than we ever have. Our employers are throwing new terminology at us, like health savings accounts, health reimbursement accounts, and high-deductible health plans. They tell us these plans will be better for us in the long term and will allow us to save money for retirement. The premiums we are paying continue to increase, and we believe that no one is capable of truly controlling the cost of healthcare. For the first time, we are starting to understand our employers' frustration with healthcare costs.

This is increasing our interest in what we are spending our healthcare dollars on. At The Leede Research Group, we often tell our provider clients that consumers are currently like a bear that is being stuck in the ribs with a stick. They are starting to feel the pain of the stick. They are not sure why the stick is prodding them or what they can do to stop it. They are becoming mad and at some point will lash out and take action to stop the pain. That lashing out will drive the healthcare tsunami.

Our studies find that most of us are currently spending what we believe to be between 20% and 30% of our personal income on healthcare. Some national studies indicate that this may actually be underestimated, depending upon how spending is categorized, such as discerning between prescriptions, over-the-counter medications, and other drugstore items. Recent surveys completed by The Leede Research Group indicate that some consumers, especially those under age 35, expect to be paying as much as half of their costs personally in as little as five years. All age groups believe their personal costs will increase. This is even true of those on Medicare and Medicaid, which may indicate that consumers believe that those programs will have problems in the near future. This may result in them paying at least a portion of their own care in the future.

So now what? We are coming to understand that we have to take responsibility for making good decisions about our healthcare. We really do not know what that means. We really do not have anyone to turn to in order to gain a better understanding of our situation and how to address it. While we may question our physician about some of this, we know he or she is far too busy to engage in a dialogue about how to use health services efficiently.

We have an interesting perception of physicians in this process of change. In many ways we believe they are victims of the system the same way we are. Qualitative research has demonstrated that many of us feel sorry for physicians and believe they are being forced to endure overscheduling and are not able to spend the time they should or want to with us. We do not blame them for that, but rather the large provider networks they are often a part of. It appears that this attitude actually strengthens the bond we have with our physician, as we feel there is common ground.

We see quality differently than the providers do. In the vacuum of not understanding how to measure quality, most consumers look to customer-service-related metrics to measure their satisfaction. Was the doctor nice to my family and me? Did he or she know my children's names? Did he or she listen to me and hear all of my concerns? Was the waiting room comfortable? Did we have to wait long? One of the major paradoxes in healthcare is that the industry measures quality based upon tangible care outcomes while consumers are measuring interpersonal exchanges. Many consumers believe healthcare is a parity product—quality is pretty much consistent. Loyalty and word-of-mouth are predominately recommendations driven not by medical quality, but by bedside manner and personal experience.

The media are bombarding us with information on the rising cost of healthcare. We see stories every day about how the current trends cannot continue without leading to disaster. Politicians are making healthcare the major issue in the 2008 campaign. In many ways, the issue would be even stronger if it were not for the war in Iraq. There are again discussions of national healthcare, and some states, including Wisconsin, have plans for universal coverage provided by or supported by state government.

We have a hard time understanding the way the industry works. Some of us no longer have insurance of any kind. If we go to a hospital or clinic, the first question we are asked in admissions is whether or not we have insurance. If we do not, we appear to be relegated to another area of the office where we are often treated like second-class citizens because we have chosen to pay for our care personally rather than pay rising insurance costs. Young, healthy consumers or those with the financial resources to cover basic care needs do this because the cost of insurance premiums outweighs their annual usage.

A recent participant in one of our patient focus groups was a young man who did not have coverage. He said, "I really don't understand healthcare providers. I am paying [you] in cash and because I do not have insurance I know I am paying [you] the highest rate that [you] offer because I am not part of a large group. Yet, while I should be your best customer, [you] treat me like a second-class citizen." It was an interesting perception and reflects why consumers have problems understanding healthcare and the way it works. What other industry treats a cash customer paying a premium price like this? This is what will drive the coming tsunami. This treatment of the consumer is what will leave some providers wondering what has happened to their market share.

Most of us as individuals do not have a clue what to do next. We pay premiums for our care, so why is it that when we need to use services they still cost more money, and the costs are higher than they were just a few years ago? Why can't a provider tell us how much a procedure will cost? How can we reduce our costs of care and benefit from the new programs like health savings accounts? Who can help us? The bear is getting angry. Can action be far behind? This action will determine the speed, force, and direction of the tsunami.

Part of the confusion is the fact that this product—healthcare—is different from most of the products we purchase. With most products, we understand we have a need and search for products to meet that need. We then review the features and prices of the products, review our budgets, and pick the item that best meets our needs. When we try to do this in healthcare, we find that nothing seems to fit.

We really do not know what product or service we need. We have a health issue and in most cases we are not sure what should be done to address the issue. We rely on our physician to help us identify the specific need and direct us to the appropriate care. Even when the doctor tells us what services are needed, it is difficult for us to use our normal consumer experience to take the next steps.

While we might know what services we need, we generally have no clue about what they cost. We also do not know who is qualified to provide the needed services. In the past, we simply let our doctors tell us what to do and we followed their directions. We did not pay for the service, so we were not terribly concerned about price or options. This situation is changing now that we are paying for more of our own care.

Another factor is that, unlike groceries or gasoline, we do not purchase healthcare services on a regular basis. The infrequency of the purchase and the basic human belief that we will never need health services means that we do not take much time to learn about them or how to consume the needed services. Many consumers have been on managed care plans and often have difficulty differentiating between care and the coverage that pays for it.

For some time now, a number of parties have pushed and prodded us to become better consumers of healthcare. This started with our employers, who bore the brunt of our costs and were heavily impacted by our lack of understanding and incorrect or unmonitored use of related services. They tried to offer education to help us use the system efficiently and find ways to control utilization and costs, but we generally did not respond to these opportunities and felt little need to change our habits.

We do understand that more people than ever before have problems with healthcare coverage. We understand that many no longer have insurance and even those who do are often underinsured. An April 2007 study of more than 2,000 adults polled by *WSJ Online* and *Harris Interactive* showed that three-quarters of respondents supported a variety of activities that would expand healthcare coverage to more Americans. These ranged from mandating employer coverage to greater government intervention and extended Medicare and Medicaid coverage. But concerns arose about small employers in this process, with two-thirds of respondents indicating that mandating employer coverage could force small employers out of business. Respondents were split on whether the risk was worth the potential gain.

We now find that we must become better consumers of healthcare. We need to know what the appropriate care is and when to use it. We are coming to understand that the dollars that we do not spend today will be kept in our accounts and will grow for the future. The funds that we do not use before retirement can help us offset costs when we reach age 65. We will learn how to consume this new product and eventually get good at it because we are now getting the right motivation to do so. The tsunami will be both a driver and result of that change.

12 The Consumer's Perception of Quality Evolves

The concept of quality is no stranger to healthcare. The industry, like many others, has gone through the quality revolution and made significant strides in improving quality in the system. This is true whether the measurement is made by technical and empirical tools or through the voice of the customer in patient satisfaction programs. Healthcare, once thought to be a unique type of business entity, has now adopted many of the same quality control and improvement techniques as seen in other industries, such as Six Sigma and lean production.

The quality movement of the 1980s impacted the healthcare industry as well. Tracking the common themes in patient satisfaction reveals that much of the early work on improvement was tied to basic processes within the healthcare system. Hospitals worked to improve admissions processes, timely delivery of hot meals, room cleanliness, and the like.

Physicians' offices and clinics improved things such as access, office hours, parking, and waiting times. At this time, there were fairly significant differences in patients' perceptions of quality between players.

This was, in part, a factor of the production mentality. The industry had spent years building infrastructure and technology, and its goal was to fill the capacity it had built. This had a significant impact on the overscheduled and impersonal environment that the industry became known for and to which the consumer became accustomed. The goal was to maximize use and generate the volume that the capacity allowed, thus maximizing the return on investment made in that production capacity.

"Your watch is fine. We set our clocks back an hour just to make you wait."

Quality became the mantra of the industry. Providers could differentiate themselves on quality, and players such as the Mayo Clinic, Johns Hopkins, and Marshfield Clinic were seen as quality innovators and leaders, giving them a premium position in the marketplace. The perception of quality was generally built not only on being a large provider organization, but also on involvement in cutting-edge medical research and tapping charitable foundations to fund research, growth, and community involvement.

These high-quality providers set the bar for other organizations to strive for in their quality processes. On the other end of the scale were generally small organizations, often in rural or inner-city settings. While their quality was not necessarily bad, it was not on the same level as that of industry leaders. These players operated within their markets and within the resources they had available, both monetary and human. They were generally well received in their communities, but clearly not on par with the leaders in their category.

Organizations such as the Joint Commission, formerly the Joint Commission on Accreditation of Hospital Organizations (JCAHO), also stepped up quality standards and moved aggressively to increase quality in the industry as a whole. Others, such as the National Association on Healthcare Quality (NAHQ), were formed to support the growing movement on all levels. The Agency for Healthcare Research and Quality (AHRQ) was also formed to gather information on quality and share that with both providers and consumers. AHRQ is also charged with managing the Consumer Assessment of

Healthcare Providers and Systems (CAHPS) program, a public-private initiative to develop standardized surveys of patients' experiences with ambulatory and facility-level care. Quality has clearly become a key expectation of the industry and the patient.

Many of the process and procedural issues of the system were corrected by the late eighties and early nineties. Patients determined the next steps in the evolution of patient satisfaction.

So, with process and procedures corrected, the next step was to look for quality in the relationships that the patient has with the system at every contact point, from admittance to follow-up treatment. The next round of patient satisfaction measurement was characterized by measuring relationships and developing plans to improve them. The concept of the patient as a customer and potential advocate for the provider was born.

Changes in healthcare, while on a different timeline, mirrored those of other industries, which also went through a quality movement and therefore understood the need to build strong relationships with customers. Industries have found value in creating strong customer service. When the customer service playing field leveled, companies moved on to other areas in need of change. For some, the next progression was generating strong customer experiences. The goal was to create customers who are so loyal and happy that they become advocates for the business or product, using word-of-mouth referrals to bring other customers to the organization.

Consumers are king regardless of the industry, whether it is government, manufacturing, retail, or service. While each industry has a different type of consumer, the process of consumption is usually similar. Many industries have been forced to adapt to the changing will and desire of consumers. Consumers vote in the only way they know how, with their dollars. It is not so surprising that eventually the same process would have to happen in healthcare. The only thing missing was the power of the vote. That is now changing as we begin to spend more of our own dollars on care. This is the driver of the coming tsunami. The consumer model is the only system we as consumers truly understand. Whether in full or in part, the consumer model will impact the future of healthcare. The question is how strongly and how quickly.

At the same time, something else started to happen in the industry—consolidation. Integrated health networks formed, bringing together hospitals, clinics, pharmacies, home health, hospice, rehab, and a variety of other tertiary services. These new, large systems developed better procedures and quality standards. Added resources quickly improved quality and raised the standards of quality in the industry. This process went on throughout the nineties.

Quality continues to be an important driver of organizations and a commitment made by their management teams. Physicians and specialists take great pride in their commitment to quality and continue to stress its importance to their administrative teams and staff. Quality is spoken loudly and clearly in marketing and communications from provider organizations, as it is assumed that quality must be important to the patient. But what happens when an entire industry is seen as delivering quality?

Our extensive consumer research in the healthcare industry suggests that the consumer now assumes quality from virtually any healthcare system. They have a basic belief that in today's competitive environment, a provider could not be where it is without having a quality organization. While it is important for the consumer to hear quality in the messages communicated by providers, it is no longer an item that can be used to differentiate between major players in a category. This has created some challenges for healthcare marketers who have worked for years to differentiate themselves on the basis of quality.

A recent study of 1,000 consumers conducted for a major provider organization showed overall satisfaction with the respondents' primary care physicians to be 6.2 on a 7-point scale. When comparing the individual satisfaction levels of the top four provider networks in the same geographic area, all providers received a rating of 6.2 or higher. Furthermore, the difference between the four largest physician networks was less than two-tenths of a point. Satisfaction and quality perceptions are clearly at their peak, and there is little difference between the major players from the perspective of the patient. All are seen to have outstanding quality overall.

Focus groups conducted with patients in a variety of settings confirm this position. Participants indicate that all providers offer quality. They all generally have new facilities and have expanded. They all have access to the latest tools and technologies. They are all perceived to be providing a quality outcome for their patients. There is generally a comfort level in using any provider in a given market. This is true even though consumers are generally resistant to changing their primary care provider.

If this is the case, how do we choose whom we use and where we go for care? Our recent work indicates that the most critical component of the use of healthcare services is the relationship the patient has with his or her primary care physician. Generally, between 70% and 85% of consumers believe they have a relationship with a primary care physician. This varies by age group, with younger patients being less likely to have a physician.

In focus groups, patients tell us that they rely on their physician as a primary contact with the healthcare system. They believe this doctor knows the right tools to access and the resources needed to provide their care. If a specialist is needed, they can count on their doctor to make the proper referral. If tests are needed, they rely on the doctor to identify specific tests and the best sources for these procedures. Research indicates that most patients will follow the recommendations and directions of their physicians. This makes them an important gatekeeper in the healthcare process.

Since consumers believe that there is quality in all of the healthcare systems, it would seem that it should not matter where they go for care. Since they are not paying directly for that care, they really are not concerned with costs, so that is not a factor either. Why would they not follow the recommendations and directions of their physician with whom they have built a long-term relationship? Research indicates that most consumers over 35 years of age have had a physician relationship for longer than 10 years. They may not have visited that doctor for the past 5 years, yet they perceive him or her to be "their" doctor. The question is whether this relationship process will change as the almighty dollar comes into the equation.

Another question that arises is whether consumers' perspectives will change once they start to pay for their own care. Will they be willing to alter their current physician relationship if it will save their family money on healthcare costs? Consumerism may change the parameters of the physician relationship. At the very least it may bring price into the equation, which has not been a factor in the past.

The Leede Research Group believes that the inclusion of price may change the basis and perspective of the relationship. When someone else was paying for the care, it may have been acceptable to have long wait times and rushed, impersonal care. That may change when the consumer is footing the bill, thus lowering satisfaction scores and driving greater focus on customer service.

The Leede Research Group does extensive work in the process known as customer value analysis (CVA), as developed by Brad Gale, author of *Managing Customer Value*. Gale, a veteran quality expert who has a history of involvement with the Malcolm Baldridge National Quality Award and the Conference Board's Total Quality Management Center, always believed that quality was something ultimately defined by customers. He set about developing a customer satisfaction tool that looks at a real-world environment. One important measurement included in a CVA is how the respondent values quality versus price. A question gives the respondent 100 points to allocate between the two. The response is used to determine the slope of a "fair value line" that helps evaluate each competitor in the marketplace.

The Leede Research Group was one of the first research firms to bring this tool to the healthcare provider arena. Medical manufacturers had used it for some time. It could not be used in consumer environments for providers, as the consumer had no sense of price, not even a significant perception. In the past three years, however, as consumers have been bombarded with information on the importance of cost, this has changed.

The Leede Research Group has used this tool in both employer and consumer settings, with very consistent results. Consumers generally place about two-thirds of their points on quality and one-third on price. The employers are consistently in the 50/50 range. We believe we will see the consumer move to a similar position over time.

A flat line indicated by a 50/50 response is generally found in industries that have what we call a "commodity mentality."

A commodity mentality occurs when a consumer, whether business or individual, feels there is little difference between the qualities of the players that provide that product. Lack of differentiation on quality leaves price as the primary decision factor in a purchase, making price increases difficult.

The property and casualty (P&C) insurance industry is one that typically operates in this type of marketplace. Often customers do not even know the actual insurer they are using for P&C coverage because the coverage is provided through an agent or broker with whom they have a primary relationship. That relationship actually becomes the important decision factor and overshadows the identity of the insurer. The broker can often move the customer between insurers with little more than a recommendation and minor cost savings.

Could this be the future of the healthcare industry? Could it be that the relationship the patient has with his or her primary care physician becomes the dominant factor in the selection and use of healthcare services? Quality has created an equal playing field. Does this mean that price is the only remaining differentiator for the consumer? This could have dire implications for the industry moving forward.

Will physicians be able to move patients between provider networks with simple referrals? What role will price play in this type of environment? We have seen a general commoditization of many segments of the U.S. economy. It has impacted almost every industry segment as consumers come to believe there is little difference in quality between products and players, especially when they believe that all players are providing high quality. This creates unique challenges that could be difficult for healthcare providers to deal with in the short term and possibly beyond.

We doubt that many today would call healthcare a commodity. It is highly personal and customized to the individual. A person delivers it, which is often the hardest variable to control. There must be perceived differences that will continue to allow providers to drive choice and secure a premium for their offerings. Yet from a research perspective, the signs and trends being seen in healthcare are indicative of trends seen in other industries.

Let's consider the concept of commodity further. In general, a commodity is something for which there is a market demand, but which is supplied without qualitative differentiation. Prices of commodities are determined as a function of their market as a whole; however, the process of commoditization is ongoing as markets evolve. In essence, commoditization occurs when a product or service becomes undifferentiated across its supply base by the sharing of knowledge necessary to acquire or produce it efficiently. As such, many products that formerly carried premium margins, have become commodities, such as generic pharmaceuticals and silicon chips.

From the consumer's perspective, the functional attributes of healthcare are a commodity. Testing, diagnosis, and treatment all appear to have little differentiation in the consumer's mind. In that respect, healthcare is healthcare. The inherent interpersonal or emotional aspects of healthcare delivery are most meaningful to consumers. Rightly or wrongly, consumers are more likely to judge the quality of their physician by his or her smile, tone of voice, and manner as they are by his or her experience and efficiency in treating illness. Patients want to be cared about, not just cared for.

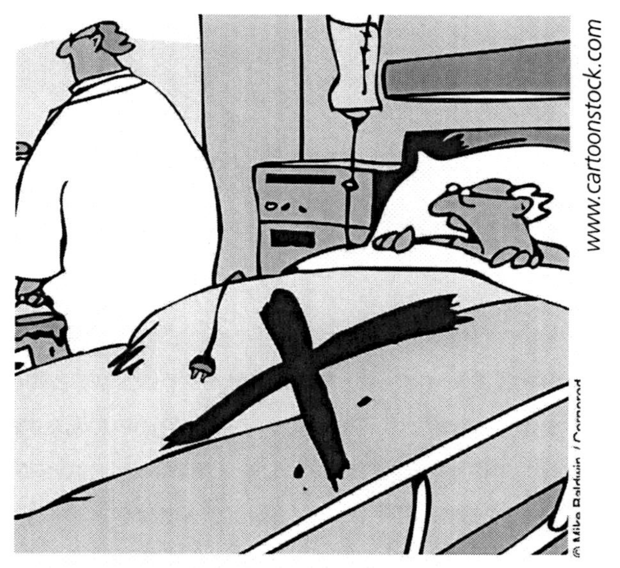

"You've got a lousy bedside manner."

A trend is emerging and there are organizations embracing the personal customer service model. Without a significant investment in resources, there are providers who cater to their patients' wants and not just needs. These providers are in high demand, have spectacular word-of-mouth equity, and command above average market share and revenue. They may be the players that ride the tsunami to a new and higher ground.

13 Consumers Take Their Rightful Place

While the patient is an integral part of the healthcare process, the industry has never truly viewed patients as consumers or customers. The idea of calling people consumers or customers, rather than patients, is a relatively new concept in the healthcare realm. The perspective of viewing customers as patients is based upon the fact that they needed care or had a condition. There was also the subtler fact that patients generally did not pay for their care. In the true sense of the word, the real customers for most providers were the employers and insurers.

Healthcare as an industry has undergone an interesting progression through the years. In the 1980s, the healthcare industry saw itself as unique and special. Businesses and consultants that served the healthcare industry had to be specialists in healthcare. The idea that those with experience in other industries could bring that knowledge and apply it to healthcare was seen as foreign.

As healthcare progressed through the quality-improvement process in the 1980s and 1990s, administrators began to see that tools and techniques from other successful industries could be applied to healthcare. While these tools often needed to be adjusted to the unique set of variables in the industry, they did still apply. The perspective of the industry changed, and administrators began seeking the best consultants and tools that business had to offer. Healthcare brought CEO's and top managers from outside the industry who offered a different perspective and set of business expertise. This cross-pollination helped bring new ideas to healthcare and moved it to improve through acceptance of best practices from other industries.

So the patient has now become the customer. The industry has come to learn that it has much to gain by meeting and exceeding the needs and wants of customers. This began initially as driving consumer choice. In many markets, large employers offered several plan designs and options from which employees could choose. Being a preferred network generated greater selection and increased the provider's share of the market. This was the earliest form of consumerism, even though the consumer was not paying for a significant portion of the cost.

As customers begin to spend more of their own dollars on healthcare, they will vote, as they do in all other industries, with their wallets. Consumers will have newfound power when they understand the value of that vote and use it to change the industry. This will change everything from the way care is delivered to the information available on procedures and their cost. Consumerism will generate greater transparency in an industry that has a high degree of confusion under present conditions.

Society has seen glimpses of what true consumerism may look like in healthcare. Take laser eye surgery, for example. When first developed, the new technology of laser eye surgery was a miracle. The ability to eliminate a patient's use of glasses and restore vision to perfect levels was exciting. It was not a medical need, though, and as such would not be covered under traditional insurance. So, the consumer would spend his or her own money for this procedure.

The developers of laser technology understood the need to follow a more traditional consumer model in bringing this medical product to the market. People would have to come up with the funding for this miracle from their own pockets. The product had to be marketed much like any other high-end consumer product. Initial costs for this treatment began at almost $5,000 per eye.

Consumers began purchasing the new procedure and were thrilled with the results. Satisfied consumers generated positive word of mouth, a powerful tool in health services, which was then supported by mass advertising featuring testimonials. This, in turn, created increased interest, and consumers became more informed about the service. Knowledge of the procedure allowed them to shop for options and make an informed decision.

Competing technologies came into the market. More eye-care professionals bought into the technology, creating added competition, greater capacity, and wider access. Advertising and marketing activities increased awareness of the procedure and its benefits. We have now moved from the introductory stage of this product to a more mature product. As happens with any product in this situation, prices have come down. In some markets, a patient can have the procedure completed for less than $1,000 per eye. Further cost reductions are expected.

While traditional healthcare services cannot be directly compared to this product setting, there are similarities. The advent of greater interest generates an appetite for information. By getting that information, consumers become knowledgeable, giving them the power to make better decisions. This brave new world will eventually come to the healthcare industry.

We must acknowledge that we will make true consumer decisions in healthcare only when we have the luxury to do so. The biggest impact will be on basic care and procedures that are used for preventive care and general treatment of minor conditions. Consumerism will also impact any type of elective care and treatment that we may have the option to use. It will change the way these are offered and selected.

When a significant health event occurs, especially a sudden need, we are not likely to behave like a typical consumer. It is then that we will act like a patient in the truest sense of the word. We will look for our doctor to get us into and through the healthcare system. We will want the best testing and care he or she knows of and will not question or worry about the cost. While we may ask more questions and be more involved in related decisions, it is unlikely that we will act against our doctor's recommendations or even seek a second opinion.

One thing we may have to watch in this new world of consumerism is that providers may look for ways to shift their costs to meet the changing pricing model demanded by the consumer. This may lead to increased costs for more significant care and treatment where the consumer will not question pricing. Other gatekeepers may be needed, such as employers and insurers, to maintain control over costs.

Some of these significant health events will result in the need for care relating to a chronic condition. This will place significant pressure on our newly found consumerism. We will find that we have ongoing costs related to care, and because of the high-deductible environment, we will be paying for many of them from our savings mechanisms. This will force us to be better users of long-term services and will have great impact on the providers and industries that serve those conditions.

Another factor may help drive the change that has been initiated by employer cost shifting. Some studies indicate that women more than men are having issues with the current model, due in part to the differences in healthcare needs between men and women. Women make up a higher percentage of the part-time workforce and also tend to earn less then men, which impacts their ability to be insured and their ability to pay for both insurance and care.

A 2005 study by the Commonwealth Fund, a group that supports independent research in the healthcare industry to promote performance, indicates that women have more problematic healthcare issues. Young women are the most likely group to be uninsured. They are less likely to have coverage through their own employers and more likely to access a spouse's coverage. Women also tend to be more frequent users of health services and, therefore, are more likely to have out-of-pocket costs. The report indicates that policy makers should consider this in future decisions.

The study further documents the differences in women's use of health services, indicating that women are generally almost 50% more likely to take prescription medications. This is even more prevalent in the 19 to 29 age group, where women are more than three times more likely to take prescription medication than their male counterparts. This difference has significant impact on a woman's experience with the healthcare system and the costs associated with her care. With rising deductibles and changing plan designs, women are also more likely to feel the financial impact.

The study indicates that women are also more likely than men to have access issues because of these related costs. Women tend to not fill prescriptions, skip tests, or not see a physician or specialist when needed. This is not a good model for the future if current conditions were to persist.

Women are also more likely to have debt issues associated with their medical bills. The study finds that nearly two in five women report medical bill problems. Among uninsured women, 56% indicate difficulty in paying bills. A quarter of women indicate that they cannot pay their medical bills. This is more common for women under age 50, which may reflect their payment of both their own bills and those of dependent children. Smart providers are already providing "women's services" as a key tool to position them for the future.

Women in general have been more involved in consumerism than men. They tend to be better consumers of most goods and services and have the potential to generate a tremendous amount of change in healthcare. If women decide to become strong, confident consumers of health services, the provider world will be a different place.

We believe that this discrepancy between men and women has the potential to dramatically increase both the size and speed of the coming tsunami. The female head of household has traditionally been considered the primary decision maker for health services. If these women are experiencing greater issues and challenges with the current model, it is likely that they will be key players in changing that model.

Consumers are poised to take their rightful place as the main customers and payers in healthcare services. They will first accept this new position casually, doing business much as they do today. As time progresses and they begin to understand their new position and responsibility, it is likely that their behavior will change. We believe that this will lead to higher expectations of the industry and the experiences they have using it. Suddenly, service delivery standards that were acceptable when employers were bearing the burden of costs may no longer be acceptable. These consumers may not revolt; they may simply find alternatives that better meet their needs and expectations. It will fall to the providers to understand the change and strive to retain their share of healthcare spending. Consumers will vote with their dollars and the winners will be the successes of the post-tsunami era.

14 Retailers Learn the Game

This is one of the most extensive chapters in this book for one simple reason—it describes the most obvious indication of significant change in the healthcare industry. Retail medicine is the ultimate example of true healthcare consumerism. Extensive activity is taking place in this category, and the business strategy behind it will form the landscape after the tsunami. Information on this subject was literally coming to us daily during the writing of this book. We hope that you will share our interest in how a new business category develops and how decisions made today will shape the future.

A 2007 Booz Allen Hamilton study on healthcare consumerism indicates that consumers who spend their own money on healthcare are more aware of both quality and cost differences between providers, but are just starting to act on that knowledge. The study shows that these consumers are more likely to extend the time they take planning before actually using services. Researchers believe that this will continue as consumers evaluate options and make better decisions.

The study indicates that consumers expect those on the supply side of healthcare to compete, but on different levels. Providers are expected to compete more on quality than on price. Those in insurance and pharmaceuticals are expected to compete heavily on price. However, the study indicates that consumers feel there is little information to help them make these key decisions.

The work indicates that physicians feel that consumerism is a top issue and will impact their practices heavily in the next three to five years. Physicians believe it will have more impact than the highly touted "pay for performance" systems. Only 20% believe that the consumerism process will result in better-quality care or stronger relationships.

While oil and water may not mix, retail and healthcare may. That is the bet being made both by leaders in the new field of retail healthcare and by many major retail organizations such as Walgreen's, CVS/pharmacy and Wal-Mart. These players are investing millions of dollars in the new segment, and are already battling for the position of national leader in retail healthcare.

In April of 2007, Wal-Mart announced that it would add 400 retail clinics to its chain in the next year and as many as 2,000 in the next five to seven years by partnering with both national retail clinic organizations and local provider networks. This announcement was one of the early shots fired across the bow of the traditional care delivery system in America. Wal-Mart viewed the move as an important step in offering "customer solutions to America's healthcare crisis," on the heels of its popular $4 prescription program that ignited huge competition in the industry.

Pharmacy operations have purchased two of the top three major retail clinic chains. The leader, MinuteClinic, was purchased by CVS Corporation in 2006. The transaction was valued at around $170 million dollars, each of the existing 83 locations being worth around $2 million. This was at a time when MinuteClinic as a whole was showing a loss of $20 million dollars. MinuteClinic opened its 100th location in October 2006 and its 200th location in August 2007. Michael Howe, CEO of MinuteClinic, has said the company will reach 400 locations by the end of 2007 and ultimately will open more than 2,500 locations, based on consumer demand. This demonstrates how traditional care is integrating with the increasing expenditures on prescription medications.

CVS is not only betting its future on retail clinics; in 2007 it also outbid Express Scripts in the purchase of CareMark, the second largest pharmacy benefits manager in the country. This significantly improves its market position and ability to negotiate with payers.

Take Care Health Systems, seen by some as the number two competitor, will open 200 locations in the next year and another 1,400 by the end of 2008. It is partnering with Walgreens, which finally purchased the company in May of 2007 under undisclosed terms.

It is not clear how this will impact relationships built with RediClinic, another industry leader. RediClinic is also partnering with Walgreens in some locations. It is also a budding partner with Target in clinics being developed for that chain. The pharmacy relationships with these chains could give RediClinic access to over 10,000 locations across the United States. RediClinic said that it expects to open 500 new locations by 2009, enabling the company to bring its convenient and affordable nonemergency care to millions of consumers throughout the United States. This expansion will occur partially through its existing partnerships with Wal-Mart, H-E-B, and Duane Reade as well as through a new partnership with Walgreens, the nation's largest drug store chain.

A new player called AeroClinic seeks to bring retail clinics to major U.S. airports, providing well-care and prescription-filling services (through an on-site pharmacy), in addition to minor ill-care services. Its goal is to provide superior and swift health services to commercial airline passengers and the airport communities that support the safety and well-being of commercial air travelers. This is changing the way care is delivered and who will profit from that care.

The players in this new category are impressive, to say the least. They range from industry healthcare leaders from major networks, to fast-food CEOs with a history in franchising, to leaders in the computer industry with a focus on technology. Steve Case, of America Online fame, formed an organization called Revolution Health, which is currently backing at least three of these major clinic chains.

Experts project that by the end of 2008, there will be one retail clinic for every two to three hospital locations in the United States. This expansion is ever-increasing and will create a network of competitors to traditional providers that will exceed them in total numbers and possibly in preferential locations. This will be a factor of the coming tsunami and a result of it.

So why would the consumer want to use health services in a retail setting? The answer today truly comes down to a single word: *convenience*. Our work clearly indicates that this is the driving force in the movement toward retail healthcare. Consumers like the idea of not having to make appointments and getting care in a setting that fits with their other activities.

Our qualitative research indicates that this convenience has a number of benefits, including being able to complete more tasks with fewer trips. There is also convenience from the perspective that the consumer can get diagnosis, treatment, and prescriptions often in a single trip. Parents of sick children find this to be very attractive, as they do not have to take their sick children in and out of vehicles multiple times.

In the late 1990s, providers found themselves in a dilemma. Clinics and physician offices were addressing significant access issues. The waiting times for appointments were often weeks or even months. In some markets and/or specialties, this is still the case today. Strong dissatisfaction also grew with the waiting times in doctors' offices. Finally, patients indicated that they felt rushed when they were seen and they did not get to spend quality time with their physician. Most providers redesigned their scheduling process to increase satisfaction, leading to a system that allows the physician to have 10% of his or her time free in any day to see immediate-need patients. The balance of unused time can then be used to spend more time with patients who did have appointments.

It took the healthcare system some time to recognize and fix the access problem. In the meantime, consumers began to expect that they would not be able to see their doctor or specialist in a timely manner. They changed their expectations to avoid disappointment and assumed that this situation would not improve. This led consumers to change the way in which they accessed the healthcare system.

Then consumers found their own solution to the problem. They simply started using emergency services, urgent care programs, and walk-in clinics. These segments of care have seen tremendous growth in the past 10 years, and indirectly demonstrated to outside players that there are other ways of delivering acceptable healthcare to consumers. The trade-off was the intimacy of the personal relationship with their physician versus access to immediate, convenient care. This is an early demonstration that consumers value convenience over cost in some settings.

A 2005 report by the Centers for Disease Control indicates that the average wait time in an emergency room is 46 minutes. That report also indicates that visits reached a record high in 2003, at 114 million. This took place in an environment where the number of emergency departments at hospitals had actually declined by 12% in 10 years. An increase in demand while there is a decrease in supply will cause continued stress on the delivery system. This trend also allowed for continued growth in the pricing of emergency department services.

The report indicates that the major users of emergency departments (EDs) tend to be those who are over 65 years of age, those who have lower incomes, and those covered by government-sponsored insurance. The study notes that the network of EDs in the United States is often viewed as the safety net of care for those below the poverty line.

The younger population began migrating to newer alternatives. Many hospitals began offering urgent care services, which direct patients with less critical needs to another area of the facility. In many cases this was a result of employer pressure on hospitals to give them some relief from the high costs of nonemergent ED visits. Urgent care clinics gained popularity and became common in a relatively short period of time.

Much of the healthcare industry did not go into the business of walk-in clinics or even urgent care facilities willingly. Providers were happy to offer these services through traditional EDs, which generated significant revenues. Employer pressure and competitive placement generated the broad move to these new delivery methods. Many hospital-based providers lost significant revenue streams in this process—yet another example of the ability of the provider to disregard the needs of the market because of the third-party-payer system.

The next evolution of the provider system addressing the need for convenience and broader access to services was the walk-in clinic. This was a natural outcome of patients' desires for greater access to their primary care physicians at non-traditional hours. Providers found these to be solid tools to relieve overscheduled physicians and to access patients from other providers. It also helped drive business to their pharmacies, as many began offering onsite or near-site prescriptions. Good locations within easy access of shopping and banking were the most popular.

Our studies have shown an interesting dichotomy with regard to the consumer. As discussed earlier, about 80% of consumers believe they have a relationship with a physician. Of those, 70% believe they could call their doctor and be seen the same day if there was a need. Having said that, 50% have used the services of a walk-in clinic in the past year. This increases to 70% for consumers under age 35. The percentage increases even more if the household has children. That is an important indicator for healthcare and its relation to the size of the tsunami and the world after it passes. There is clearly something missing in the current delivery system.

Convenience is clearly driving the new movements in both traditional and retail healthcare. Along with this are basic differences in the way consumers under 35 years of age think and make decisions. The Leede Research Group has seen evidence of this in studies addressing issues ranging from healthcare to dining to consumer products. This consumer group is strongly driven by convenience. These consumers tend to be more brand oriented, but less brand loyal. While they seek out brands they know, they are more likely to use multiple brands than are their older counterparts. These fundamental differences are important to the future of healthcare and many other industries.

Take, for example, a single mother with a small child who knows her daughter has an ear infection. It is not the first time and she knows all the signs. She needs a prescription eardrop medication. She has a number of choices under the current delivery system. First, she could call her family physician or pediatrician and make an appointment. She probably could be seen that day, but would have to conform to some type of schedule that fits the physician more than it does her.

The next option is to go to the local hospital's ED or urgent care facility, a cumbersome and time-consuming process where the wait times for nonemergency care average longer than one hour. Younger populations generally are not choosing this option unless they believe they require serious care or diagnostics.

Another option is going to the nearest walk-in clinic. This is a serious option for most parents. They can go without a structured appointment at a time that fits their needs. They generally have the choice of more than one location from a number of area providers. They will select the one that best meets their immediate needs. Convenience of location is generally a key factor, based on where they are at the time, whether at home or work. Insurance coverage is also a factor in this decision.

The final option is new and becoming more popular. They can go to a retail location such as a CVS/pharmacy and visit a MinuteClinic location where a nurse practitioner diagnoses the problem and prescribes medication in less than 20 minutes. A prescription for drops is automatically transferred to the pharmacy desk at the store. Within 30 minutes the woman is back in her car, taking her child and the prescription home. She has taken her sick child out of the car seat only once, as opposed to at least two times under the previous examples.

She paid about $49 for this visit, plus the cost of medication. She likely paid by credit card and is not concerned about insurance coverage. The emotional benefit to the consumer is gaining a sense of control. Service is quick, convenient, and focused on consumer needs. Welcome to the new world of retail healthcare.

Studies show that there are many attractive aspects to this alternative. Consumers like the fact that these retail locations offer them the opportunity to complete other errands along with meeting their healthcare needs. They also like the convenience of having the prescription available at the same site and at the same time as the visit. While this is available in some traditional walk-in clinics, patients often have to make another trip to an outside pharmacy, which takes extra time and travel. This is often challenging, especially with an infant or young child in tow who has to be strapped in and taken out at every stop.

Many consumers actually like the fact that they can pay for care by credit card. It appears that it is worth the $49 to many consumers to avoid filling out additional paperwork or wading through insurance billing forms they often do not understand. Once again, convenience is king and consumers are willing to pay for it.

While the retail category is relatively new, activity has been highly competitive. No one has yet risen to the surface and taken over a national leadership position in retail healthcare. More than a dozen companies are currently vying for positions in the market and generating strong growth. This growth is coming from both the retail healthcare business and from strong interest by major retailers such as Wal-Mart, Target, and West Coast grocery leader, Albertsons.

Some players on the provider side are not sitting on the sidelines and missing this opportunity. Aurora Health Care in Milwaukee is cited as one provider network considering regional and possibly national entry into the field. Many other provider networks are considering retail locations for more traditional walk-in clinics to provide added convenience to those who need services. A study of 1,000 consumers indicated that they combined other activities such as banking or grocery shopping with visits to their physician an average of 42% of the time. This is again higher with the younger population.

Providers are also working to make the consumer visit to a traditional walk-in clinic more convenient. Those without on-site pharmacies are starting to have the top 20 to 50 prescriptions on hand so that patients do not have to make added trips. Others offer free delivery to make the care of the patient convenient and completed with a single trip. This is clearly a response to the retail clinic environment and is driving the process of change.

Some critics think that putting funding in the hands of consumers will result in them using fewer services. Some of this reduction may be appropriate, but others fear that consumers will put off care that could prevent later serious illness and conditions. Although no data exist to support the concerns over this issue, we must take it very seriously.

If consumers don't manage their retirement funding, can we assume they will manage their long-term healthcare funding? The American Savings Education Council's 2004 report, *Saving and Retirement in America*, states that among all workers, 45% have less than $25,000 in savings and investments (aside from equity in primary residences). According to a 2002 survey by the Consumer Federation of America, 25% of U.S. households have net assets of less than $10,000.

One thing that early research is showing is that consumers, when spending their own money, are much more likely to use generic medications than when they were covered under traditional insurance. This could represent a significant change for the pharmaceutical companies that could impact earnings and the development of new medications.

There are also issues with the traditional gatekeeper model used by most providers. The healthcare delivery system was actually a fairly simple and tight model until recent years. Patients had a relationship with a family physician that they used for care needs. It was the physician's role to guide his or her patients through any needs they had. Networks set up a specific structure to control and leverage this process. The physician was generally charged with keeping the patient within the network and system unless there were items that could not be delivered there. This kept as much money as possible within the provider's network.

That model has changed dramatically in recent years. Walk-in clinics have been a big part of the change. Consumers are flocking to these clinics and are generally not concerned whether they are or are not a part of their physician's network. This further supports the concept that consumers view the literal treatment of illness as a commodity. Single-parent households have also contributed to the trend. Often children may live with one parent but are covered under the other parent's insurance. This may require different network usage. Both usage patterns expose consumers to new networks and new options. Both have the potential to break the steerage that is part of the traditional gatekeeping model.

Retail clinics have the same potential to impact usage. These clinics provide a specific set of services and limit the level of care they can provide. When a more serious need arises, these facilities must direct the patient to a qualified provider. Giving retail clinics a significant influence in patient steerage will serve to bust through the old gatekeeping model closely held by many provider networks. Gatekeeping equals referrals and referrals equal revenue. This is an important tool and resource that will be built into the business model.

In 2005, the top three retail clinic chains signed an agreement with the American Academy of Family Physicians (AAFP). The purpose of this agreement was to establish quality standards for care at these retail locations. They agreed upon a set of services that are appropriate for the retail environment. They agreed that each facility would be under the direction of a physician, who would not be permanently on-site, but who would be available if needed.

The major retail chains also came to an agreement on the referral process for patients with conditions that may require referral to a specialist or other medical facility. The agreement calls for the first level of referral to be to the patient's existing primary care physician. If the patient does not have a current relationship, or the patient does not feel he or she can gain access, the clinic is then free to refer the customer to another professional. The next in line is the medical director for that retail clinic. This makes the position very attractive for a physician who is looking to build his or her practice and patient volume. After the medical director, the clinic would be free to send patients to any source it chose.

National studies are showing that 20% to 30% of patients accessing retail clinics do not have a physician relationship or loyalty. If 20% of patients do not have a physician relationship, this means that one in five people passing through these retail clinics may be referred to other physicians. This is a significant opportunity, one that retail clinics know and understand the value of. They will clearly develop relationships with traditional providers who can benefit from this new form of steerage. It should be noted that this could be an added income stream for these new operations.

While we have indicated that consumers appear to be willing to spend their own money in these retail clinics, most clinics will accept insurance payments. In fact, some insurers are actually suggesting that patients use these new clinics. Some employers are already offering to drop deductible charges for employees who use these services. Cost is the simple reason for this. Employers are finding that the savings in costs compared to an ED visit clearly offset the deductible costs.

These clinics have fixed prices for different types of care and treatment and they are generally well below the costs of traditional providers. This results in savings for insurers as well. Acceptance and even promotion by the insurance industry and employers has the potential to speed the growth of retail operations.

Not all of the physician community is happy with this evolution of care. In June 2007, the Illinois chapter of the American Medical Association (AMA) called for the national organization to request a ban on retail operations or, if a ban was not imposed, significant restrictions and governance of the system. The organization cites concerns about patient safety and quality of care. While it is too early to tell what the result of this action will be, the AMA has considerable might in terms of legislative impact. Its lobbying resources alone could put these new operations into a holding pattern. While not stopping the industry, they could slow its growth and give members more time to respond with competitive offerings. They could also put significant financial pressure on new players and impact their business model.

While the concept of retail clinics has been around for several years, it was not until just recently that physicians called for a stop to this form of care. It is also interesting that this request would take place two years after the AAFP and the leading three retail organizations signed agreements. Clearly, the concern may be more about control of patients and their dollars than anything else. History has generally shown that the consumer's will triumphs over all.

Consumerism is a retail term. Consumers have begun to take their rightful place in healthcare. While quality of care, the right products and services, and strong customer satisfaction have been important to the industry for years, they have always been missing one key component: consumers' ability to vote with their dollars. This voting process is now becoming a reality as HSAs and CDHPs move to center stage. The word *consumerism* is about to take on a whole new meaning to the providers of healthcare. Retailers may understand this process best and are poised to acquire their share of the healthcare market. The question is, at whose expense?

Good retailers have a knack for identifying the unmet needs of the consumer and using them to develop new products and services. While the current retail clinic model provides common services, testing, and inoculations, a new model could include other services of value to consumers, such as education tools and programs that can help consumers be better users of healthcare services. The new model might also include wellness and prevention tools, which will grow in popularity as the public sees the financial value of staying healthy. Retail clinics could become retail health centers offering a wide range of services and tools.

One player in the retail category that hopes to create a new service tier is Solantic, based in Orlando, Florida. The new tier would fall between the newly developed retail clinics and the traditional care providers, who are generally part of a network offering walk-in clinics, urgent care facilities, or both. Solantic is developing a chain of independent urgent care clinics staffed by physicians and offering a more traditional and full range of services. At first glance you might wonder what makes this different from existing provider clinics. The difference sought by Solantic is to offer a more complete range of services at strong locations that offer maximum convenience for the customer. The company seeks to staff these locations with physicians who are selected via special personality profiles to give superior customer service.

The founder of Solantic, Richard Scott, was the original founder of Columbia/HCA, which became the largest health-care network in the country. He has partnered with Florida television anchor Karen Bowling to launch 15 clinics across the state. Scott has a clear understanding of the healthcare industry and its strengths and weaknesses. Others clearly believe in his concept, as the new company in the summer of 2007 received a $100 million venture capital investment, which will allow it to build or acquire 40 more locations—12 within the next year. Solantic will then be a significant player in the category and one that will have the potential to build an entire new tier of services that pose an even greater threat to traditional provider networks.

It is believed that the recent investment made by New York–based venture capital firm Welsch, Carson, Anderson & Stowe (WCA&S) may not be the only financial resources coming to the new company. WCA&S manages more than $16 billion in venture capital. Scott's connections from HCA could make him a significant player in the future of the industry. His knowledge of the industry and related connections make him a formidable competitor, whether in the healthcare or retail segment.

The Solantic concept assumes that the consumer benefits from access to a broader range of services than can be offered in the new retail clinics. It also assumes that the range of services is more important than the access to those services in a retail setting. Some of the work completed by The Leede Research Group seems to confirm this, though it has not been conducted on a national basis. Solantic could create a new care delivery model that truly puts customers first and seeks to make their experience the primary indicator of quality in the system. Solantic seeks to provide service in an hour or less and will post waiting times on digital dashboards in its facilities. It will even offer beepers that allow patients to do other errands and be notified when their visit is near. The concept could be a powerful tool and, if successful, could set the bar higher for traditional providers and how they deliver services. Solantic could create a leading organization in the delivery of care in the new healthcare landscape.

We believe this positioning has a great deal of potential and value. All current quality research generally indicates that consumers are satisfied with their healthcare experience. This is true in their use of walk-in and urgent care services. Where the retail clinics are making their mark is generally a straight factor of convenience. There is no appointment needed. Consumers have confidence that the wait times will be minimal. They also believe they can leave in a short period of time with needed prescriptions and will not have to make an additional stop.

If convenience and access to prescriptions are the only true variables, the Solantic offering could tap those aspects while offering a deeper level of service. This could be a very attractive option for consumers spending their own dollars on care.

As consumers begin to understand the significance of spending their own money for care and treatment, they are going to be looking for ways to maximize the value of what they are spending. They are going to be looking for ways to save money, to get more for less, to understand how to be good consumers. Retailers like Wal-Mart have been teaching us these things for years. Why would the consumer not look to players like this in healthcare as well? The retailer may be able to play a significant role in the future of healthcare.

We may also see savvy retailers looking for additional opportunities to capture dollars from consumers' growing HSAs. Retailers may begin to offer educational materials and even programming to help increase consumers' understanding of their care and treatment. This could include books and electronic materials on a variety of topics, from consumerism, to health management, to care and treatment of chronic conditions. Educating the consumer will have value to both the consumer and the retailer, and it expands the offering, making the overall retail experience more attractive.

Retailers may also begin to offer tools to help consumers track and manage their HSAs. These could range from logbooks to track eligible expenses and save receipts needed in the case of an audit to electronic tools such as software programs that would serve a similar purpose and also allow for the tracking of personal health records. Tools could even include computer software that could create models to help consumers assess the value of different healthcare treatments and options. They could even evaluate different lifestyle changes and help determine both the health and financial benefits of change. Several companies are entering this new space, and the category promises strong growth as these plans grow in popularity.

Retailers even have the potential to become outlets for medical devices, such as home monitoring and telemonitoring tools. These are generally offered through professional services in the current market, but could be adapted to a more retail presence. This would help make retail locations a more complete stop for consumer healthcare needs.

Retailers may also go after what we believe will be a growing market for wellness and prevention services. Young consumers are coming to realize that maintaining their health now offers financial incentives along with a better quality of life when they get older. This is generating a stronger interest in wellness. Programs that can help consumers monitor and maintain health could be a solid opportunity for both retailers and service providers.

There is also the issue of alternative medicine entering the retail environment. HSA dollars can be used for services ranging from chiropractic care to acupuncture. Even massage therapy is covered in the proper environment. Providers of these services could find that migrating to a retail environment will enhance their access and increase convenience for consumers. This could create multi-practice retail clinics that provide a range of services, all of which are covered under HSAs. This would provide a one-stop shop for a variety of needs.

Retailers have a clear advantage in the world after the tsunami. They understand how to communicate with and market to the consumer. They are accustomed to competing for dollars and may even leverage healthcare retail spending with other retail offers and opportunities. Bringing together retail healthcare and traditional consumer retail habits could offer a strong incentive and added convenience. They will offer the traditional healthcare providers a challenging competitor that seeks to tap the billions of dollars that are now available through HSAs.

The future of retail healthcare may be the future of consumerism itself. Will traditional providers get the message? Will they respond with a Band-Aid or will they make a meaningful change in the way they deliver services to better meet the needs of the newly empowered consumer? The answer to these questions will literally shape the future of healthcare delivery in America and will change its major players. As they say in the trade publications, "Watch for Retail Clinics to Roll into a Location Near You!"

15 How Timing Could Impact Size

By now we hope you have developed an acute awareness of the pressure that has been building in healthcare for almost 20 years. The pressure is about to be released. The question is whether the release will be as subtle as when it built, or whether there will be an explosion of energy that will result in a tsunami effect that will change the landscape of healthcare forever. We believe the latter will take place, as the perfect set of conditions is coming together for the tsunami to hit, and it will bring about key changes in the current system.

Employer Frustration and Cost Shifting

This is not a new issue and has been around for years. Many employers reached their limits in the late 1990s, after years of trying everything they could to help control costs and create a process under which healthcare coverage fit their budgets. They tried managed care, business coalitions, wellness programs, direct contracting, and various other tools. Yet costs continued to rise by double-digit rates annually.

Employers have reached a point of frustration and believe that no one, including providers, insurers, or government, has the ability to fix the current situation. Employers indicate in qualitative research that they are simply looking for the easiest and most efficient way to spend their healthcare dollars without generating significant complaints from employees. They are willing to look at new solutions, but history has created skepticism and they are no longer aggressively seeking solutions. This is especially true of small- and mid-sized employers, who feel they have fewer options and little, if any, control. Given that small business is the engine of U.S. economic growth, responsible for 75% of all new jobs, this attitude is of vital importance.

Employers feel that employees cannot be good partners in controlling costs today or in the future. They believe this is because employees do not understand how to use health services efficiently and do not take steps to improve their health. They feel that employees do not care and do not understand even the basics that drive costs.

The frustration and inability to deal with continued rising costs have led employers, both large and small, to begin shifting the burden of payment to employees. Whether through CDHPs, defined contribution plans, or just simple changes in plan design and premium share, employers are shifting the financial burden to employees. They are doing so in part due to financial necessity, and in part as a hope that employees will become more responsible once they are spending their own dollars. Either way, the change is occurring.

Employers are essentially pushing employees out of the nest. They are saying, "Here are your dollars—let's see if you can do better." They are forcing employees to make the decisions they should have been making for years in hopes that this process will at least slow the continuing advance of costs. Employers understand that the cost of employee care has become one of the most expensive areas of their business and has the potential to drag them under if change does not occur.

We believe that this growing segment of employers will have significant impact on the size and speed of the wave. Projected growth of CDHPs will throw significant numbers of employees into consumer markets. This will increase the size of the movement exponentially and speed the process of change, as employees have no choice but to become better consumers.

Government Legislation and Intervention

Government action may be the wildcard in the equation. Government may have the greatest direct control over the size and timing of the wave, because legislative efforts related to healthcare could change the perspective of all the players involved. As noted in Chapter 8, millions of dollars are spent annually on lobbying by the healthcare industry. These efforts can have a direct impact on the future.

Remember that the United States started down this path once before. The medical savings sccounts (MSAs) of the 1980s were an attempt to do for the self-employed what is now being done for all employers. The goal was to put the money in the hands of consumers and, by allowing them to spend their own money, control future costs.

The idea of the MSA may have come from healthcare analysts who were concerned about the problem of "overinsurance." They believed overinsurance was raising the cost of healthcare. They further reasoned that if patients (as opposed to third-party payers) paid their own medical expenses, the cost of healthcare would decrease—an early sign of healthcare consumerism.

During the early 1990s, organizations such as the National Center for Policy Analysis in Dallas and insurance companies such as Golden Rule Insurance Company in Indianapolis began to promote the passage of MSA legislation that would allow for tax-free contributions to the savings accounts. Even though Congress was under Republican control, and even though the MSA was central to the Republicans' healthcare agenda, a federal MSA law failed to materialize during the 1990s. Powerful lobbying forces managed to keep it out of the national scene.

Congress did approve a pilot program for MSAs as a part of the Health Insurance Portability and Accountability Act (HIPAA) in 1996. Some individual states passed MSA legislation during the 1990s. Missouri was the first state to do so, in 1993. By 1998, 25 states had some form of MSA legislation offering a state tax break to those who opened an account.

Some industries and powerful players would prefer that the current healthcare delivery system remain the same. We may see lobbying by some players in the provider and insurance industries who seek to slow the process of change or derail it completely. We believe this will be a challenging task, considering the number of industries involved and the momentum that consumerism has gained with both employers and consumers.

A recent call by the Illinois chapter of the AMA to impose legislative restrictions on retail clinics is an example of intervention that could delay the release of the tsunami and possibly reduce its size. Lobbying and the legislative response to such activities could slow the progress of retail providers. Opponents might also recognize that the movement to CDHPs is driving this change and seek to stop that. All of this could tie the process of change up in legislation for years.

Government could also speed the process of change. As the largest single customer of the healthcare industry, it has a great deal at stake. If legislation were to make CDHPs more attractive to both employers and consumers, there could be a significant advance in both the size and speed of the tsunami. Allowing employers to fund individual plans could move more consumers to the individual market. The elections of 2008 are likely to have a significant impact on the future role of government in this process.

Consumer Demand

Perhaps the most important of all the factors, consumer demand may also determine the timing and size of the wave. The will of consumers will drive change in the industry and could be key to creating needed changes in legislation and the political environment. If consumers see the value in taking responsibility for their healthcare spending, they will participate in the continued growth of HSAs and CDHPs, therefore accelerating the process of consumerism.

The Leede Research Group's recent work with healthcare consumers shows that while the penetration of high-deductible plans is still below 10%, there is strong awareness among those under 55 years of age. We also see that those under age 35 have the strongest interest in these plans' use. This is logical, as they are healthy and have the most to gain by spending their own funds and building large accounts.

What may be different this time around is the true frustration that both the employer and consumer are experiencing with regard to healthcare. In the 1980s and 1990s, we seldom heard consumers speak of cost. Their health concerns centered on serious or chronic conditions such as cancer and heart disease. Only a small percentage of consumers even thought about cost. Today, opinion surveys show that cost has become the number-one issue within the spectrum of insurance, healthcare, and prescription medications that overshadows all others. This momentum may be enough to keep the current movement on track and the power of consumerism growing.

Interest in Healthcare From Other Industries

This is possibly the subtlest of the factors and often goes unnoticed. The multi billion-dollar business of healthcare is attracting a lot of attention from banks, financial service providers, non-health insurers, manufacturing companies, online companies, the service sector, and retail. All are trying to see what they can do to get their share of these dollars by offering their contribution to the solution.

Even where the dollars themselves will be housed until used is turning into a battleground between traditional financial institutions and the new charters being given to members of the insurance industry. Other nontraditional sources may also try to get into the game. Why would Wal-Mart not want to offer health savings accounts? It has had several requests for banking charters turned down by regulators under pressure from the banking industry. Could health savings accounts tied to retail clinic expansions be the silver bullet that gets the company the charter it has been seeking for so long?

As other industries continue to get involved in healthcare, they bring with them new ideas and techniques. These are applied to the healthcare model and often result in ideas and concepts that had not been considered by the industry in the past. Consider the burgeoning category of patient remote monitoring. In this setting, patients may be able to spend recovery time in their homes instead of hospitals or other skilled facilities. They can be monitored with innovative equipment being developed by manufacturers in a number of segments. These tools take advantage of high-speed communications lines or the Internet, and allow for real-time monitoring of patients that would previously have taken place in hospitals or rehab facilities.

While these tools and applications will never replace complex care found in an intensive care unit (ICU), they may replace some facility-based care and monitoring for a variety of chronic conditions and thus help manage the overall cost of care. We are already seeing the impact on traditional care, with some networks offering virtual ICU environments where specialists monitor patients from another community. GE Healthcare is a leader in this technology, and demand is growing. Remote monitoring could touch almost one-third of American households that house someone with a chronic condition. This is just the next step in the evolution of care meant to address consumer interest in both cost and convenience.

Even the technology giant Microsoft is working to ensure that it is not left out of this growing new industry. It has recently announced its Health Vault project, which is a tool to house and use patient information and connect patients and medical professionals in an online environment. It could be a key factor in the growth, as Microsoft's touch-points and marketing power could mainstream such tools very quickly.

Cross-pollination from other industries will improve healthcare and begin to give consumers the things they truly want, often before they want them. Services will be delivered in a way that may be far different from what we are used to. Some household names will be forgotten, while others will emerge. A new environment will change the way we see health and our future.

In addition, as other industries get involved in the wave of change, they will promote their role in the process. Financial institutions will promote their health savings accounts. Insurers will promote their high-deductible health plans. Education and wellness programs will promote the value of good health and consumerism. This groundswell of information and marketing will increase awareness and drive positioning in this new category.

Interest from other industries is a key factor in the size and speed of the tsunami. Competition is a wonderful phenomenon that speeds up many processes as companies race to be the first to reach new ground and meet new needs. As these varied industries come together, the speed of change will increase and the size of the tsunami will grow.

Traditional Provider Response

The final factor impacting the size and speed of the coming tsunami is the traditional providers themselves. How they respond to the growing consumer movement has the potential to slow its progression or move it along with increasing speed and power.

Evidence already shows that traditional providers understand the change and want to be part of the new landscape. Leaders such as Alegent Healthcare are stepping up their activities to be part of the consumerism movement. Alegent understands the need, both as a provider of services and as a large employer that has felt the impact of rising healthcare costs for its employees.

Retail-like medicine from a traditional provider does have some potential benefit. It would likely be focused more on the convenience of access and would include more physician-based care, offering a broader base of services than are currently available from existing retail clinics. This could strengthen the middle tier currently under development by Solantic, which seeks to offer an option somewhere between that of the retail clinics and traditional providers.

If traditional providers get into the game, it could change the fundamental way the industry cares for patients, likely generating more pricing transparency and greater access to quality-of-care information. This has a tremendous potential to advance the tsunami and give it significant energy to generate change.

We believe that trends and innovation are coming together in a way that could form the perfect storm, so to speak. This perfect storm could bring everything together in the next three to five years and generate a tremendous wave of change in American society. The trends are all in place and are all starting to converge. If nothing comes along to stop them, we will see a new era in healthcare—one that will leave few players unchanged.

16 What the World May Look Like After the Tsunami

Imagine that it has happened. A tsunami of undefined size and strength has come along and changed the healthcare system in the United States forever. This new world represents a frontier where no player is left unchanged. Each of the key segments has undergone changes, to the extent possible in its environment.

The key feature of this new world is that consumers are spending his or her own money. The concept of the "magic card" that covers whatever we need is gone for most Americans under age 65. Instead, Americans seek options and care that provide value and help maintain and improve health. Because of the continued growth of HSAs, consumers now understand that there is a personal financial benefit to being good consumers of healthcare. They also understand that being healthy improves not only their physical quality of life, but also their financial quality of life.

All the key players will have different roles in the new health-care world created by the tsunami. They will adapt to the new model of consumerism and will create markets that more closely resemble those of other consumer products and services. For some, this will be only a minor change. For others, such as the providers, this will represent a new way of doing business that is foreign to them, but one they will have to learn.

www.cartoonstock.com

Consumers

Consumers of health services have changed the way they use the system. Most are now on some type of a high-deductible health plan. They have an HSA to which both they and their employer contribute. They now understand that the money not used for their care stays in the account and grows, which can help address future health needs and can also be used as another source of funding for retirement. Recent rule changes have allowed consumers to do a one-time rollover from their IRAs or retirement accounts into their HSAs. This addresses the issue of under-funded accounts in the early years of the program and increases consumer confidence. As the HSAs grow, consumers can change their insurance coverage and take advantage of cost savings from even higher deductibles.

Americans take a more active interest in their care and the costs associated with it. They do more research online to understand their condition and the options for care related to it. They ask more questions, justifying and verifying the need for tests and what they cost. They seek alternatives to high-cost options, such as chiropractic care and acupuncture, both covered under the new plans.

Consumers do something previously unheard of—they compare costs between providers. Information is more readily available than ever before, which brings together pricing information from providers within a region. While pricing information is only available on basic care items, it will set consumers' perspectives of provider costs and will impact the selection and use of broader services as well. This tool allows consumers to identify and compare services, satisfaction, and outcomes to select the best value in a provider for different needs.

A variety of websites are coming online at both regional and national levels that help consumers make better decisions about their healthcare. Some insurance companies are developing a tiered approach in which providers are ranked on cost and quality and policyholders are given incentives to use the most efficient care. Along with information from insurance sites, there are government-sponsored sites and private sites such as *Compareabill.com,* a site currently under development in the Midwest, which will offer a regional source for price transparency information. These sites will arm consumers with key information they need to make better decisions. They will move consumers from judging quality based on word of mouth to making a judgment based on fact, which will eventually help better differentiate providers.

Consumers will seek to better understand the medications they take. As they spend their own funds, they are more likely to consider and use generic medications to control costs. They may also question the true need for medications and ask their physicians for lower-cost alternatives. They will migrate to pharmacies that offer value in meeting prescription and other health needs. Some of these will be retail clinics and nontraditional providers.

Additionally, consumers will consider and use more forms of alternative medicine. HSAs allow coverage of a variety of alternatives ranging from chiropractic care to massage therapy to acupuncture and even some vision and cosmetic procedures. As consumers spend more dollars in these areas, mainstream providers may start to add alternative health providers to their networks in an effort to retain funds being lost. Consumers will find solutions that work for them in terms of both quality outcomes and cost.

In this new world, consumers will have one added responsibility. Current rules require that consumers keep all receipts for care through their HSAs. Receipts will have to be kept for extended periods of time, as a tax audit would include a review of deductible health expenses. Records must be kept indefinitely, just as if they were tax records. Technically, they are—and are subject to review in an audit, as they are using tax-free dollars. This need will likely create new tools and software systems to help manage accounts and related expenses.

There will be a variety of new online tools to help in this process. The tools may range from education programs to prevention to systems that allow the integration of electronic medical records from providers with other activities being done to improve health quality. The concept of personal health records (PHR) is already generating significant activity from Web developers and entrepreneurs alike, creating new tools and options for improving health.

One significant question looms on the consumer horizon. Will consumers continue to show fierce loyalty to their primary care physicians? If there are other alternatives that offer lower-cost care, will they forgo the physician-patient relationship in the interest of cost savings? These questions will be difficult to answer but will determine whether the traditional gatekeeping processes currently being used by provider networks have survived the force of the tsunami. If consumers favor cost over the relationship, the current gatekeeping system of controlling patients could implode. Provider systems will need to find new and innovative ways to bring patients into their system and retain their business.

Providers

The most dramatic impact is on this group. Provider systems have undergone the greatest amount of change. Providers are forced to meet consumer needs in ways that they have not in the past. Consumers respond to the provider system differently now that they are spending their own money. Consumer expectations have changed, and the keys to generating satisfaction and loyalty have moved to more traditional consumer interests.

Changing expectations may put pressure on the current system of patient satisfaction measurement being used in the industry. The Leede Research Group is already receiving anecdotal information from its provider clients indicating that the current relationship-based system is maxing out in terms of value and the ability to generate positive change. These tools have been in place for at least the past 5 years, and the industry may have already seen incremental gains from improving the relationship the physicians and staff have with the patient. We believe that the next generation of patient-satisfaction efforts will be based on consumerism—looking at the experience the patient had and how to improve it.

One of the biggest changes is that providers are forced to adhere to a single pricing structure. Transparent pricing involves publishing rates for different basic services accessed by consumers. Many consumers will use this information to make decisions concerning provider selection. Consumers will also begin to ask for a written quote on more complex procedures prior to selecting a provider. Providers may even be asked to guarantee a quote on a "not-to-exceed" basis.

Regardless, discounting of services to large customers has not ended. Large employers and insurers continue to negotiate discounts based on volume. Direct contracting between employers and providers also continues. While true single-tier pricing may not be possible, there will be far less variation in the pricing for different groups than is seen in the current setting.

Hospitals and clinics compete for healthcare dollars with retailers, pharmacies, chiropractors, and other organizations that seek to offer value-added alternative health services. The only limitations are those set by the reimbursement structure of HSAs.

Other professionals, such as physician assistants and nurse practitioners, will provide some of the services currently provided by a family physician. These services are delivered in nontraditional settings such as retail locations or specially designed freestanding quick clinics and urgent care centers within healthcare networks, designed to be convenient for consumers with minor needs.

For many, their physician continues to be their primary contact point with the healthcare system, and they continue to rely on that relationship to access services and technology. This is especially true for those who have significant medical needs requiring access to a specialist or hospitalization. This part of the healthcare system changes more slowly, as it is not as directly impacted by consumer decisions.

Physicians have greater flexibility in their schedules to spend more quality time with patients and better meet their needs. We commonly hear in focus groups that patients generally feel doctors are too rushed and do not give patients the time and attention that they would like. New delivery models may start to off-load tasks, due to service and cost issues, that do not require physician skills.

Advertising plays an increased role in the competitive environment. As choice plays a larger role, many providers strive to generate awareness and brand equity through advertising.

Consumer expectations of their physicians increases and physicians are under added pressure to be personable and provide strong customer service. Consumers seek physicians who are service oriented—physicians who know their name and those of their children and can recall their last visit. Those who listen and make the patient part of the decision-making process will be highly successful.

Electronic medical records (EMR) systems play an important part in service delivery in this future. This tool allows physicians to have detailed patient information and records at their fingertips via tablet computers. They have both information on the patient's health and personal information, allowing them to personalize the visit and improve the customer experience. The use of this tool must be balanced against the quality time spent directly with the patient. EMR technology also allows patients to access their medical records online at any time.

The government is already behind the movement to EMR, offering reimbursement incentives for some providers who use it. It cites the fact that EMR reduces medical errors and helps improve quality outcomes by generating better instructions and greater patient compliance. This movement is likely to continue, and EMR should become mainstream in the next five years.

Unfortunately, some providers will close their doors. We believe that more healthcare capacity exists than the market really needs. To this point, capacity has been filled under the third-party-payer model, but consumer-driven care will not allow that practice to continue. Reduced volumes and an inability to increase prices could force some providers to close, as they cannot support the significant infrastructure they have built, especially in some small and mid-sized markets with competing networks.

Another outcome of this process may be further consolidation of healthcare provider networks. As patients question the need for tests, eliminate duplication, and even postpone care to save money, providers will experience financial losses. Those that do not have a sound financial position may find they cannot survive without consolidating. Entire networks of care may even be eliminated.

Leveraging limited staff and eliminating duplicated technology may be the only way networks can survive. This is especially true when future shortages of medical professionals are taken into account. Acute shortages of nurses and even physicians are projected at a time when baby boomers, the largest population of seniors ever seen in the United States history, are moving through the health system.

Physician income will likely decrease as well. Consumers are going to force prices down and this will impact the income of physicians. Physicians may be forced to accept lower salaries in order to remain competitive, especially when some services may no longer require the use of a physician. They may have to find ways to reduce costs and increase efficiency within their practices.

This phenomenon is already evident in the state of Massachusetts, which established the first universal healthcare program in the nation. While it has been in place for only a few months, news stories already indicate that there is an exodus of physicians from the state as they find they can no longer make their normal income under the newly imposed conditions. This could be an issue for the future, impacting everything from existing physicians to attendance at medical schools.

This type of shift may return some level of entrepreneurship to the job of being a physician. In speaking with physicians in preparation for writing this book, we heard of some doctors considering a return to a more personal level of care for their patients, including making house calls. The concept is that if consumers find retail clinics to be convenient, what could be more convenient than being seen in their own homes? This could lead to more physicians remaining independent and could change the face of healthcare delivery, returning it to a model similar to care of days gone by. The pendulum swings back under the power of consumers.

Another important issue may also come to a head because of the issues related to consumerism in healthcare. Many in the industry point to medical malpractice laws and the related costs of insurance as one of the drivers of rising costs. Physicians point out that while they make exceptional wages, they also have significant risks and costs related to insurance coverage, leading some to leave the field or stop practicing certain types of medicine. When the new consumerism hits, there may be an increased need to address this issue and set limits for medical malpractice.

Providers are likely to enter the retail market in some shape or form. They will seek to take advantage of their experience and the relationships they have with physicians. They will work to provide services that offer the benefits of retail with the added quality of their physician network and foundational tools and technology. This may lead to a blending of retail and healthcare offerings into a true consumer-driven product delivered in a more consumer-friendly manner.

Retailers

Retailers have the most to gain from the post-tsunami era. Retail entry into the healthcare market will likely generate significant interest as consumers take advantage of the convenience of getting care while performing other daily activities. Retailers are likely to start with the foundational services currently being offered and then expand them based on strong consumer research and an understanding of customer needs. They will offer other tools and programs through these locations that support health and healthy lifestyles, including smoking cessation, weight loss, and overcoming other negative lifestyle behaviors.

It is also possible that retail clinics may become educators of healthcare consumers. A tremendous opportunity exists for retailers to position themselves as part of the solution to rising healthcare costs. Education could position them as leaders and as an alternative to the traditional delivery model that raised costs for years. They are uniquely positioned to take advantage of decades of complacency related to costs. This could give retailers a significant new stream of revenue and their share of the new wealth of healthcare dollars that are available from HSAs.

Online retailers also want to acquire their share of this new marketplace. These retailers will offer everything from education programs to expense tracking. Some of these products will be printed, some electronic. Some will bring multiple formats together to offer complete systems. Revenue is available through helping consumers evolve in this process. Sharp retailers will understand how to offer superior products to a public in need.

Online players will also want to play a role in the process. Firms such as drugstore.com offer online pharmacies especially designed for HSA holders. These sites offer tracking tools and greater ease of use that may be attractive to the new consumer. It is clear that retailers will influence the delivery of healthcare well into the future.

Insurers

Insurance will change dramatically, yet slowly, during the post-tsunami period. Insurers are already seeing the change in their industry and will face further significant changes in the future. They are seeing high-deductible plans growing rapidly, even though they have made little to no investment in marketing them. Consumers will not suddenly jump to high-deductible plans. Older consumers may never go, opting to stay with existing coverage until they transition to Medicare. The change to consumer-driven plans will accelerate but will take time.

Younger consumers will move to these plans sooner, perhaps in the next three to five years, after being pushed along by employers who want to shift costs. Higher-income consumers in better health will use the tax benefits of HSAs as another financial planning tool. This will change the size and nature of the risk pool for more traditional products and may require legislative action to correct.

Over time, HSA users will amass significant balances in their accounts. As the balances increase, consumers will seek higher deductibles in their health plans, allowing them to reduce insurance costs. This activity may be limited by either government regulation or the industry itself, which may not want to lose revenue streams. Competition may force insurers to offer consumers programs akin to current stop-loss insurance, which is generally sold to self-insured employers who want to adjust their risk.

Stop-loss coverage is designed to protect the policyholder from a major-loss event or the cumulative impact from a number of events put together. Policyholders can select coverage that meets their needs and budget. Stop-loss coverage kicks in if a single claim surpasses a target number or cumulative claims exceed another target during a one-year period. This coverage is currently available only to employers and insurance companies but could be extended to consumers as HSA growth occurs in the market. Extending stop-loss coverage would require legislative action.

The future appears to be swinging the insurance pendulum back in a way that is comparable to when the industry first started, which is providing coverage to reduce the risk that a person would suffer financial hardship because of a medical claim. No-frills plans are likely to be attractive to consumers who once again want to limit costs and keep dollars in their accounts.

The insurance industry is already testing new plan designs that may better fit the world after the tsunami. In July of 2007, the nation's top health insurer, UnitedHealthcare, introduced a new type of plan that actually penalizes participants for unhealthy behavior in four key areas: smoking, obesity, blood pressure, and blood sugar. The new plan sets higher deductibles for those who do not meet health standards in the key areas but allows policyholders to reduce their deductible by participating in healthy practices. This plan type may prove attractive as consumers seek ways to force themselves to improve their health.

In May of 2007, Destiny Health and AEGON Direct Marketing announced a major plan to deliver what they call "healthcare empowerment" to the nation. The agreement brings together Destiny with Stonebridge Life Insurance Company to underwrite a new plan. At the core of this new concept is the Destiny wellness program called Vitality, which encourages policyholders to improve their lifestyle choices by offering everything from lower health insurance costs to free merchandise. Destiny Health has data that prove its system delivers lower costs through wellness incentives. The new marketing agreement means the plan can be offered nationwide.

Insurers have already entered the banking field. UnitedHealth Group and the national organization of Blue Cross Blue

Shield both have bank charters. Blue Cross Blue Shield now offers Blue Bank, which offers HSA accounts, and is driven by banking tools and software from Fiserv, a leader in information tools for banking and health benefit organizations.

Blue Bank will begin by housing HSAs and later add investment options and other tools to help consumers manage their growing accounts. Blue Bank is likely to integrate long-term care offerings that can help account holders plan for the later years and manage health cost risks. Bundled services like these will evolve as the number of accounts grow and balances increase.

The insurance industry could also be a natural source for consumer education, thus creating new revenue streams as consumers seek to understand how to efficiently access and use healthcare services. While insurers do not have the outside perspective that the retail community may have, they do have existing relationships with both consumers and employers that will likely still hold their high-deductible coverage.

The same is true of prevention and wellness programs and services. Some plan designs may further integrate wellness into their structure. Consumers can use this to help improve their overall health and reduce future costs. These programs can be delivered in a variety of formats, including personal coaches, telenursing, and even online programs that integrate with healthcare provider information to track health and assist consumers in achieving key goals.

Another interesting issue tied to insurers is that of plan administration costs. This has been recently cited as one of the most significant costs leading to rate increases. More complex plans cost more to administer. The number of different plans and options offered by insurers also impacts their cost of administration. As consumers move to simpler plans with fewer frills, these plans should reduce administrative costs. It would also seem natural that there would be less variation in these plans, which, along with administrative cost reductions, should help control or even reduce the cost of coverage in the future.

Government

The largest single customer of the healthcare system in America will also be impacted by the size and force of the tsunami. Coverage provided by the government is generally for populations that are not covered under employer or private coverage, including those over age 65 and those that receive Medicaid. This currently represents just over a quarter of the population, a percentage that is expected to rise with the movement of the baby boomers through the system. The two groups will be impacted differently by the wave of change. The Medicare population will likely see the fewest changes after the tsunami. The system covers them in a way that is much like the traditional insurance plans of today. They have relative freedom of choice and will not be spending their own dollars. Therefore, they will not show consumerism behaviors and will continue to be much like the patients of today.

The government will still work to control or reduce the costs of care associated with this group. The Medicare system cannot survive under current conditions. Added costs could lead to insolvency if action is not taken.

Many studies and trials are currently under way to develop approaches to help mitigate this potential disaster. These studies range in scope from minimizing the cost of chronic diseases to developing systems with pay-for-performance models that share cost savings with providers. These efforts are likely to continue and to increase in frequency.

The Medicaid population is another matter. This population is generally made up of younger individuals who financially cannot get care through traditional means. The evolving consumer model may apply to this group and would see innovative programs that offer them the opportunity to take responsibility for their own spending and offer some incentive to use those dollars wisely. This could be a tool in cost controls and would help in addressing the overall needs of patients in the market.

As noted earlier, Medicare users pay a portion of their costs out of pocket and through supplemental coverage. Some are calling for reforms that would direct patients to highly efficient providers in an effort to reduce costs. To drive this, they are asking for a reduction of or rebates on matching costs that recipients are often required to pay. This is clearly a consumerism move and could increase the government's role in driving change.

Some experiments are also looking to change the way that Medicaid coverage is provided. The concept is that rather than providing Medicaid coverage, the government would provide funding to allow an individual to purchase coverage in the commercial market, likely some form of HDHP, thrusting this population into consumerism. These plans would likely have an HRA rather than an HSA, which would mean that unused funds would be returned to Medicaid.

Government might also benefit from the general impact of the tsunami. If consumerism is effective, the process will likely help control or even reduce costs. Consumerism will help identify and reduce overutilization, and this general pressure will benefit the government as a major customer of the system. Government may also take a closer look at consumer experiences and identify new tools and practices to help patients use services more efficiently.

Government will also play an important role in the future of legislation in healthcare and related coverage models. As consumers build higher balances in their HSAs, there will be a need to change the rules limiting deductibles on health plans to a maximum of $5,500. Plans with deductibles of $10,000, $20,000, or more will be common. This change in coverage is essential to take full advantage of the process that is being initiated. There may also be new items added to the approved list of expenditures from these accounts, including tools such as telemonitoring and other innovations that get the patient back home more quickly and reduce provider and overall costs.

Others

There will be a number of other players, some of which may not even exist yet. The financial planning industry will undergo some major changes. HSAs now present a new and powerful tool for young people to build wealth, as well as health. Financial planners will need to understand this new tool and offer innovative ways to weave it into the overall financial plans of their clients.

Online tools will likely become more prevalent as well. Some of these already exist, while some are yet to be developed or launched. Online tools will help educate consumers and help them make better choices. There will be an increase in online intervention programs to increase compliance, which are designed to ensure that patients understand their condition and related treatment, and are following critical instructions and using medications properly. Increased compliance has been proven to improve outcomes and reduce costs.

We are likely to see those involved in the home-monitoring and telemedicine areas working aggressively to take advantage of the new environment of consumerism. Their tools offer an alternative to traditional provider care and can save significant money for cost-conscious consumers. As these industries grow, the revenue will fund further product development, giving consumers even more tools and options to manage their health and related care.

We may see some new players come out of obscurity and offer consumers new options to help them manage their health and finances. What about the concept of having a personal health coach? Some wellness programs already offer this, but what if that person actually met with his or her clients like today's personal trainers do? This new offering may be an extension of personal training, offering home consultations and planning.

How about a new professional called a health planning consultant (HPC)? This new professional would bring together an understanding of financial planning with a working knowledge of wellness and prevention tools. This professional could help consumers plan for their financial futures using the power of HSAs and establish a wellness and prevention plan to help them reach goals. Consumers may be more than willing to make this investment for such a tremendous value. Compensation of HPCs could be based on incentives for both financial growth and health improvement.

Factors Influencing Speed

The retail segment could also be a factor in the speed of the tsunami. We already know retailers reach a segment of consumers who value convenience over all other factors. Retail providers are quickly learning to understand their customers and are likely to take steps to continue making their offerings more attractive. They will also seek new products and services that can tap more dollars from consumer HSAs. As they find these tools, they will put continued pressure on traditional providers and will likely increase the speed of change for all users of healthcare services.

Those who are young and/or healthy could also be a factor in the speed of change. Early research indicates that this group sees HDHPs coupled with HSAs as an attractive way to deal with two issues facing younger workers who commonly change jobs or even entire careers every few years: healthcare needs and retirement savings. HSAs offer a tool for healthy individuals to put money away for both purposes and build significant wealth as they move through different life stages.

Dual interest in HSAs is a significant factor in the speed of the tsunami. Employer change and consumer acceptance are likely to advance the movement of consumerism. They are also likely to drive changes in insurance products, as there is greater interest and competition among plans. We are already starting to see new innovations and options, including providing funds for preventive care, education, online tracking of personal health records, and more. All of these will make HDHPs more acceptable and the speed of change more rapid. The growth may also fuel legislative changes, such as increases in deductible limits, which are now capped at $5,500. Discussions with insurance industry executives indicate that we are likely to see deductibles move to $10,000 and even $20,000 in the future, as consumers build larger balances in their HSAs and no longer need the more modest deductibles. This continues to swing the insurance pendulum back to taking care of catastrophic illness or injury.

Another factor that could impact speed, noted earlier in the book, is that current healthcare issues are more heavily impacting women than men. Since women are the primary decision makers for healthcare in most households, they will likely be early responders to consumerism. They also tend to be better consumers and are more likely to become educated and seek information to help them make better decisions. This again shows great potential to increase the speed of the tsunami and the change that will result.

The actual change generated by the tsunami will also impact its speed. If employers see that the new HDHPs are not only controlling their coverage costs but are actually reducing utilization and driving down costs, more employers will jump on the bandwagon. As consumers become educated and sees opportunities, the individual market will also continue to grow. All of this will continue to put financial responsibility in the hands of the user and will speed the process of change.

Not every segment of the marketplace will drive change, however. Medicare and Medicaid enrollees will have no incentive to change their behavior. Their coverage under either commercial or government policies is such that few of their costs would be paid personally. Some wealthier individuals will make a conscious choice not to change. Finally, some older individuals with preexisting health conditions who have difficulty getting coverage under HDHPs with normal underwriting may be forced to stay under existing coverage models unless insurers offer new options.

We believe that the tsunami will begin slowly, but then pick up speed as consumers begin to understand their power and start to wield it. Once that process begins, we believe that speed will increase significantly as consumers share their knowledge and experience with others. Friends and family are key influencers in healthcare selection and decision making and thus word of mouth has the potential to significantly impact the speed of the tsunami.

17 The Physician's Role in the New Healthcare Environment

What will the role of the physician be in the new healthcare environment that will exist after the tsunami? How will the physician's role in the delivery of care and his or her relationship with the patient change? These are important questions that can only be fully answered with time and the evolution of the market and consumers. While their role in delivering care will always be a key factor in healthcare, the way in which physicians will perform their jobs and even their compensation will be impacted by the tsunami.

The physician is currently at the top of the patient relationship with the healthcare industry. The Leede Research Group has conducted extensive research with patients for more than 20 years and has come to understand the critical role that the physician-patient relationship plays in the delivery of healthcare. Approximately 80% of consumers indicate that they have a relationship with a primary care physician whom they or members of their household use for routine health matters. This percentage varies with age, as younger consumers are less likely to have the relationship, and the likelihood tends to increase with age.

A physician is the consumer's connection to the industry. Consumers sees a physician as his or her expert and contact point for significant healthcare matters. He or she also tends to be the consumer's primary source of knowledge about tools and techniques that may be needed in the course of care. The consumers has implicit trust in his or her physician and relies on him or her to navigate the healthcare system and access needed specialists and treatment. The physician has a strong ability to steer a patient through the system and direct him or her to specialists and technology that exist within the physician's own system. This important tool, called steerage, is especially effective in integrated provider networks. Steerage has played a prominent role in the success of these integrated networks as they work to keep as many healthcare dollars within their own system as possible. Individual physicians' success is tied to that of their network, so keeping the system healthy and producing is important.

Qualitative work done by The Leede Research Group uncovers a better understanding of how consumers currently see the healthcare system. Consumers believe there is high quality among all players in the healthcare arena. They believe that most facilities have the latest technology and tools, and provide access to needed specialists when a condition warrants. Consumers do not fully understand how the system works or how to access the tools, but they believe their physician will guide them through the process. Their physician is their guide and mentor and their key tool in accessing the system.

Consumers tend to have strong satisfaction with and loyalty to this physician, and is not likely to leave the relationship without some major event occurring. Our research shows that consumers typically rate their primary care physician a six or higher on a seven-point rating scale. We generally see only 8% to 12% of consumers indicating that they have changed physicians in the past year, usually because of an external occurrence, such as physician relocation or retirement, or a change in insurance coverage. Only a small percentage of this group changes because of a negative experience or lack of satisfaction.

High satisfaction usually generates a very stable marketplace for patients in most geographic areas. Most untapped patients are generally younger and do not perceive a need for a physician relationship. Therefore, shifting significant patient share is difficult by traditional methods. To effectively compete, providers must develop tactical tools to reach small pockets of patients at key contact points. The traditional gatekeeping model is already changing through a variety of new and existing delivery systems, but the coming tsunami will speed the process.

Walk-in clinics and urgent care centers often generate usage outside the relationship with the patient's primary care physician. Our research shows that although almost 70% of consumers with a primary care physician relationship believe they could see that physician the same day if needed, 50% have used walk-in type services in the past year. This percentage increases as the age of the respondent decreases. The research indicates that between 20% and 30% of usage is outside the primary care physician's network. Usage is primarily driven by convenience, as these patients do not want to take the time to call their physician or schedule an appointment.

Retail clinics are also playing a role in the transition of the typical gatekeeping model in healthcare. Most retail clinics are staffed by nurse practitioners and are designed for minor illnesses or injuries. The top chains have agreements with the American Academy of Family Physicians that establish quality parameters for these clinics and define the referral patterning that takes place when a patient requires treatment beyond the retail clinic's scope of service. This agreement stipulates that a referral should be made to the patient's existing primary care physician first. If the patient does not have such a relationship, the clinic can direct the patient to other physicians. Early research indicates that approximately 20% to 30% of users will not have a physician relationship. This represents a significant opportunity for physicians across thousands of visits annually.

We have found that single-parent households are also a factor in out-of-network usage by consumers. In many cases, one parent may have custody of the children, but the other parent provides the insurance. When both parents do not use the same network, the children may have to use a different network than the custodial parent, creating cross-usage and cross-experience in these households. Our work indicates that these households are also somewhat driven by convenience and that cross-contact tends to change their perspective in evaluating the quality of care they receive. Their cross-usage causes them to be more likely to make comparisons between providers and makes them more critical of the care they receive.

So the physician plays a significant role in the consumer's access to and relationship with the provider system. The physician is likely to be the most significant factor in the selection of specialists, since the patient will use his or her relationship to seek referrals. While patients may seek second opinions for more critical conditions, even in this environment they may ask their physician for referrals to several specialists.

The impact of the tsunami on the primary care relationship leaves some unanswered questions. In the new post-tsunami environment, consumers will spend their own dollars. How might their expectations change? What impact might this have? We believe consumers will come to expect a higher level of service than they currently receive. In focus groups, patients often discuss the need for quality time with their physicians. They believe that this is difficult to achieve under today's delivery model, as the physician's schedule is tight and patients are not given appropriate time to meet with the physician.

But interestingly, patients do not generally blame their physicians for the lack of quality time. They actually sympathize with the physicians and believe that the "system" does not give them the time they need. Patients believe physicians are overscheduled and that it is not their fault. This perception actually benefits the physician and the relationship, as both the patient and physician feel they are working toward a common goal of improving the system. It will be interesting to see if consumers give physicians the same latitude when they are paying more for their care.

We believe the changes that are likely to occur in the consumer-driven environment may have both positive and negative impact on physicians. As cost pressures mount, provider systems may have to use nonphysician staff to reduce operating costs, beneficially impacting the physicians' schedule and allowing them to spend more direct time with patients. Recent tools like electronic medical records (EMRs) give the physician access to both health and personal information that can increase the quality of the contact with a patient. As this technology evolves, the service will become more personalized and create a better experience for the patient.

Evidence shows that the negative impact of post-tsunami change may be found in the pockets of the physician. Massachusetts, the first state to adopt a universal coverage plan, is already seeing physicians leave the state because they claim they cannot make a living on low reimbursements. Consumer-driven care may cause similar financial pressures. More conscientious patients may force lower salary levels for physicians, making it more challenging for physicians to cover their basic expenses, especially medical malpractice coverage, which can cost more than $100,000 per year. We expect new interest and activity around limiting malpractice settlements and allowing for a more affordable system of insurance. This may be an essential part of the growing consumerism movement.

"Billy's father is a doctor and Tom's a malpractice lawyer."

www.cartoonstock.com

The reality is that physician income potential will decrease in the world after the tsunami. Consumer pressure on both price and utilization of services will reduce the overall budgets of most provider networks. Maintaining overhead will take a larger portion of dollars because of the reduced income, and providers will have to trim costs wherever possible. This is likely to include the salaries of physicians and other higher-paid staff members. Pay-for-performance systems will seek to reward physicians for being efficient and for generating revenue for the network. This may shift income to those physicians who can generate the best results.

A new breed of physician may also emerge after the tsunami's impact has been fully realized in the marketplace. This new physician may see an opportunity to tap the funds that consumers will hold in their HSAs. We may actually see some physicians become entrepreneurial and return to a practice style similar to that of the early 1950s and 1960s. The return of the house call could be part of these new physicians' services as they understand the value of convenience and build strong, direct relationships with their patients.

Some physicians have already shifted exclusively to a private-pay environment and make their living by providing services

KITCHEN! CHICKEN BONE! HURRY!!

to a smaller base of patients who pay directly for services used. In some cases, this care is delivered on what is called a capitation basis, where consumers pay a flat fee annually for the basic service provided by the physician. Those participating in this type of care are generally higher-income individuals who are willing to pay for better access to care and a more direct relationship. This could be an interesting business opportunity for physicians seeking an alternative to the network, employee positions of today.

Physicians who understand consumers and the new healthcare environment will benefit and will garner a higher percentage of consumer dollars. While it will be a time of great stress, it will also be one of great opportunity. Opportunities will differ in each market, based on existing providers, quality, levels of care, and, of course, price. The model for physicians after the tsunami will be one of flexibility, focus on care, and delivery of quality medicine. Those who meet and exceed consumer expectations will be successful. Those who cannot may find it challenging to exist in the new post-tsunami environment.

18 The Power of Information

The world after the tsunami will provide consumers with more information than ever before. The Internet has opened our eyes to a wealth of information on virtually every subject. Searching for medical information is one of the top uses of the Internet, and it has created a new environment for health and related education.

Sites such as *WebMD.com* have grown from nothing to become major players in the category. They have created a place for consumers to become more educated and better understand their health, conditions, and needs. They also offer those in the medical profession a place to come together and build communities based on interests and specialties.

Information on virtually any disease or condition can be found on the Web. The information provided increases medical literacy and helps families deal with chronic conditions. Communities on the Web bring together even those with the rarest conditions to provide information and support. The world is truly a smaller place because of the Internet.

Online tools are growing rapidly, coming from traditional sources and new players who see an opportunity to tap the billions of dollars that are spent on healthcare every year. The power of information may be the most significant tool in driving change in the healthcare industry. An educated consumer will make better decisions. Providing the information that consumers need to become educated and make better decisions is big business.

www.cartoonstock.com

Several key components of information are needed to help consumers make healthcare decisions, the most essential being general education. Surveys of employers and even the insurance industry have indicated that a lack of sound educational information is one barrier that prohibits employees from being better partners in controlling healthcare costs.

Another barrier to educating employees that has existed for many years is the third-party-payer system. Consumers have never had a need to become educated, as they have not had a significant enough stake in the process. Now faced with paying a larger portion of their own care expenses, consumers are developing a growing desire for tools to help them better understand what they are buying and how to do it well.

The most basic education is still required in this process. Consumers may start by understanding the options available in HDHPs and the related HSAs and HRAs. Sites are already available that can help consumers understand their options and evaluate alternatives under either group or individual coverage.

Work completed by The Leede Research Group shows that many consumers do not even understand the basics of their care and coverage and are therefore unable to access the system efficiently. They need to understand key terminology and their new responsibilities as guardians of their own healthcare dollars. They must also better understand the healthcare system and the impact their decisions may have on their care. Some consumers still believe a trip to the emergency room is the best way to access immediate services. Understanding ac cess points and related costs will give them better control of their expenditures while still providing quality care.

Once consumers understand coverage basics and how to access care, they must be taught how to be good consumers of health services. Then they need to understand when it is appropriate to access different services and how to compare these options. Many websites sponsored by the government, insurers, providers, and private parties can help consumers evaluate choices and compare both quality and price.

One of the outcomes of this stage of the education process is that consumer' perspectives of quality will start to evolve and expand beyond current perspectives. Education will teach some of the key aspects of quality and how they are demon-

"That's not what it says on the Web."

strated in both the insurance and healthcare industries. This will continue to evolve as consumers have more exposure to this type of information from a variety of sources.

Many providers will actually welcome this stronger understanding of true quality in the healthcare system. They have been frustrated with consumers' perception that virtually all providers show high levels of quality and there is little difference among them. Education may help the top providers truly differentiate themselves on the basis of quality in a meaningful way.

As consumers become educated about their role and responsibilities, they will then understand that they will truly benefit from taking better care of their health, which will open the market for wellness and prevention information. Consumers will begin to search for ways to improve their long-term health, with the focus being on better controlling their financial future.

Finally, there will also be a need to better manage the financial resources that consumerism creates. This is a more long-term need and may take 10 years to fully develop. Consumers will seek information and tools to help them manage their HSAs, with the goal of maximizing the investments for use as part of retirement planning.

Many players, including employers, insurers, and providers, have already positioned themselves to take advantage of the consumerism movement and now offer suites of tools and information programs designed to address both current and future market needs.

On October 5, 2007, a commentary in the *Wall Street Journal* by Microsoft chairman Bill Gates called for an Internet revolution for healthcare information. He notes that while society has made extraordinary advances in medical care and treatment, little has changed in the past 50 years about the way we keep medical records. The result is that an estimated 98,000 patients die annually from preventable medical errors.

He believes there is also a financial cost to this outdated system due to redundancy in testing, and injuries caused by improper treatment. This, he says, contributes to the $8,000 annual cost of healthcare per employee, which is crippling the competitiveness of American business.

Isolated and disconnected information systems in the current healthcare system make it difficult for professionals, much less patients, to effectively use the wealth of information that is gathered and tracked in the healthcare system. Gates believes that we must put people in the center of the healthcare information system. He is making this a priority and commitment at Microsoft. He envision an Internet-based system that allows providers to easily deliver information on personal health in a way anyone could access and use. He believes this is important to improving quality, reducing costs, and promoting evidence-based medicine.

Microsoft does not believe it is in a position to do this alone. It is working with other software providers and medical professionals to develop tools and systems that could fit in this new information model. The end result would be a personal health record (PHR) for all patients.

In 2005, Steve Case, a founder of AOL, started his new healthcare information site called Revolution Health. This site offers many of the features of WebMD and brings together communities of interested individuals. It contains health information, areas for providers and insurers, and a variety of educational tools that can benefit any user of healthcare services. The "My Revolution" section of the site allows users to track personal health information and store articles and other educational tools for later use.

Healthcare transparency is another key factor in the current information movement. An August 2006 Executive Order from President George Bush was designed to generate healthcare improvement by focusing on four key cornerstones:

1. Promote the adoption of interoperable health information technology.
2. Measure and publish quality information.
3. Measure and publish price information.
4. Promote quality and efficiency in care.

Mike Leavitt, secretary of the U.S. Department of Health and Human Services (DHHS), proclaimed: "Every American should have access to a full range of information about the quality and cost of their healthcare options." Government clearly believes in the power of information and putting it in the hands of citizens to improve the healthcare system.

The DHHS reports that between 2000 and 2005, the number of online sites reporting information on hospital quality almost tripled. It noted that these sites are not only destination points for consumers, but also sources for the media to access and report on quality in the industry and select markets.

The HCAHPS survey is a tool designed to standardize the measurement of the quality experience of patients using hospitals in the United States. The project is driven by CMS and will enter its initial launch phase in 2008, after 18 months of testing and development. This program is required of hospitals that receive Medicare or Medicaid compensation. It measures the hospitals on 27 quality dimensions and will be reported publicly through a national database.

Large insurers such as Aetna, Humana, and UnitedHealth Group are all working to provide policyholders with tools to compare price and quality between providers in their network. While this has not been fully successful, the work is moving the needle forward and creating the foundation for continuing the movement toward pricing transparency. The DHHS is also developing online tools that will bring together multiple sources of information into a single user-friendly source.

The physician population is not being left out of the movement to transparency. In late May 2007, California's largest private physician practice, HealthCare Partners Medical Group, posted on its website the prices of 58 common procedures. The group has 39 offices, five urgent care centers, and a freestanding surgical facility serving about 500,000 patients in southern California. This move puts significant pressure on other practices in the area to do the same.

"It feels like the right thing to do," said Robert Margolis, a founding physician and chief executive of the group, noting that the move was driven in part by the rapid expansion of retail and walk-in clinics in their service area by players such as CVS Caremark and Wal-Mart Stores. It also answers the call from President Bush for more information for consumer decision making. Margolis believes that consumerism can have only a limited impact on overall costs, because most care is used by the chronically ill who will meet their deductibles quickly and will then have no concern for costs under their insurance coverage.

In January 2007, Alegent Health, led by Wayne Sensor, launched "My Cost" as part of its network website. The purpose of this site is to bring together network pricing and quality information in a form that is easy for consumers to access and use. "My Cost" puts consumers in the center of care for the organization and offers information on more than 500 procedures within the network.

In a news release, Sensor noted, "Over the past 40 years, the health care industry has managed to create a system in which there are virtually hundreds of prices for the same procedure. Through 'My Cost' and our quality reporting, we are providing a transparent system that helps consumers understand their true cost of care, and provide information about expected outcomes for the treatments and procedures being considered."

This process is not without its challenges, as the information has to be customized for different insurance groups that utilize the network. In January, Alegent estimated that about half of consumers could access the information for their care. Another 25% should be added by mid-year. The company hopes to add professional fees for items such as anesthesiology and radiology in the next year.

Hundreds of such tools are already available or are in the development process for consumers to access healthcare information. As in many burgeoning industries, consolidation is taking place. Larger players who seek to have a competitive edge in their category are buying up progressive start-up companies. The following players represent a sample of the tools that are available and ones that we feel have the potential to move the wave of consumerism to new heights:

HSASales.com: This site is designed to help consumers and employers better understand the concept of HDHPs and related reimbursement accounts. Tom Rogala has developed a strong base of information on these programs and has the ability to both educate and provide a shopping service for those interested in making the move to high-deductible plans. He provides information that allows a consumer to look at the potential savings that can be generated by moving to an HDHP in either a group or individual setting. The site provides information for both employers and individuals.

The site also performs a valuable service as a strong educational source that helps new consumers understand how these new policies work and the key terms that are used in discussing services and benefits. This helps consumers make a decision on whether these plans are right for them. HSASales.com can even generate quotes on different options from leading players in the insurance industry. This is a one-stop shop for understanding HSAs and HDHPs.

MedEncentive.com: Many of the information tools promoting healthcare consumerism are designed to be interactive and multidimensional. MedEncentive is an innovative new tool that is designed to supplement traditional medical care and bring the patient and physician together in an important exchange of information designed to increase compliance, reduce costs, and improve medical outcomes of care and treatment.

The MedEncentive system is designed to be an add-on to an employer's or insurer's health plan. The program focuses on two key areas in which to achieve its goals: 1) evidence-based medicine and 2) information therapy. The system provides financial incentives to both the physician and the patient to engage in a dialogue.

The physician partner in the process delivers evidence-based medicine. As a participant, the physician agrees to use tools within the system that are built on extensive medical information from the nation's top providers and medical colleges, which establish proven processes for care and treatment of specific diagnoses. These treatment processes have been proven to generate quality outcomes and control costs. The physician is provided a database of such care to reference in his or her patient treatment process.

Information therapy is also a tool offered to the physicians and delivered to their patients. This is medical information on the patient's specific condition and related care designed to educate the patient and generate medical literacy in the patient population. Medical literacy is the ability of the patient to understand basic diagnosis and care information relayed by medical professionals, such as care instructions and prescription details.

A growing body of evidence indicates a direct link between medical literacy and mortality. A study by Northwestern University Feinberg School of Medicine indicates that in a study of more than 3,200 patients, those who are deemed medically illiterate have a 52% higher likelihood of dying than those considered literate. This is generally tied to chronic conditions such as asthma and diabetes. Nineteen percent of the medically literate patients died during the study period, while 40% of the medically illiterate group died—a significant difference that demonstrates the need to educate consumers on their condition, care, and treatment.

The MedEncentive system puts the doctor and patient together after every healthcare visit for a brief follow-up process. The physician can review the treatment and prescribe information tools to help the patient better understand and manage his or her condition and treatment, thus increasing literacy.

The patient completes an online interview that seeks to identify whether he or she understood their diagnosis and the instructions for care given by the physician. The process checks whether the patient received the information he or she needed and understood that information. It will also look at medications and whether patients are following medication instructions, thereby increasing compliance.

The patient receives a financial incentive in the form of a rebate on co-pay for services under his or her health insurance plan. The physician's incentive is a higher or faster reimbursement when he or she completes his or her portion of the process. This is seen as a win-win for both parties and increases participation and use.

Early studies indicate that this program can generate first-year savings as high as 10% and long-term savings of as much as 30%. Another clinical study of more than 5,000 patients currently under way will provide more empirical data on the process.

Jeffery C. Greene, founder of MedEncentives, believes that the program is a good start to addressing some fundamental problems within the healthcare industry that have led to the current crisis. He believes that poor quality of care is generated by not following evidence-based models, as well as the issue of choice made by consumers, which leads to a significant portion of the health problems seen in our society. He feels that medical illiteracy increases this problem and leads to noncompliance with care instructions.

The final issue Greene sees may be the most interesting. He believes that there is a problem with the basic alignment of incentives in the healthcare industry. He feels that it is hard to find ways to generate incentives for all partners in the process that do not create negatives for others in the process. This also addresses the basic fact that the system is set up to care for sick people, not keep people healthy. The MedEncentive system is designed to offer win-win incentives for key players, including the employer/payer.

Clearly, the amount of information available to consumers will increase exponentially as time goes on. A wealth of tools to review both quality and cost, and make the best consumer decisions for our care, will emerge. While some believe this will impact only the portion of care consumers pay for personally, we believe this is the start to a good habit that is going to impact the basic consumption of health services. Consumers are beginning to understand that the decisions they make today impact their costs for years to come. We believe consumers are smart and will start making the decisions they should have been making for years. Positive habits will eventually impact significant portions of the healthcare industry.

19 The Power of Prevention

Wellness and prevention are not new concepts to consumers. The term *wellness* was coined in the 1950s and has varying meanings. For our purpose, we will define wellness as programs and tools designed to improve the immediate and long-term health of individuals. Employers seeking to control costs by improving the overall health of their employees often established these programs. Many programs and incentives were tried in an effort to improve the wellness of the workforce, including free health club memberships, free diagnostic testing, health risk assessments, behavior modification counseling, and health education.

More recently, employers have begun offering direct financial incentives to employees who participate in healthy behaviors or make improvements. Discounts on premiums are the most common incentive, although some offer lower deductibles for those participating. Unfortunately, despite these efforts,

"I'm afraid there's not much I can do for you now. You should've come in sooner, before you got sick."

employers have not been able to motivate change in the employees who need it most.

The most common participants in wellness programs are those who are likely to participate in the healthy habits and behaviors even without an incentive to do so. These healthy individuals are simply taking advantage of the extra benefit. They are not benefiting the employer greatly, as they were the healthier of the employees in the first place. Employers do not see the return on the investment that they would if less healthy employees took on new, healthy behaviors. This return would come from lower insurance and care costs down the road.

We believe that wellness and prevention programs and tools will see a rebirth as the tsunami moves through the healthcare industry. Consumers are already beginning to see a new value in being healthy because they are finally beginning to experience the financial implications of poor health. This is already generating a new group of participants in traditional and nontraditional programs. In a recent set of focus groups completed for a large Midwestern clinic, we heard a twenty-something participant say, "I do not believe anyone in the industry has the capability to control, let alone reduce, healthcare costs. I view wellness programs and prevention as the only tool that I have to control *my* future costs." This is an astute statement and one that reflects the changing attitudes of those paying for their own care.

Renewed interest in prevention offers many new opportunities to those who specialize in such programs and tools. Consumers will likely seek ways to control their costs, and wellness is a viable solution. This is likely to increase the presence of these programs from both providers and other sources.

In 2007, we began to see that several of the major players in healthcare were coming to understand that poor health habits are playing a significant role in the increased cost of healthcare. Some estimate that as much as 70% of healthcare costs are associated with poor health habits and their later impact.

The Milken Institute, a private economic think tank, believes that the current system of treating illness after it occurs is no longer functional or economically feasible. They project that a focus on prevention and early identification could prevent

as many as 40 million cases of the top seven chronic diseases by 2023, which would reduce the treatment cost of those diseases by a projected $1.1 trillion annually. They urge that investments be made in prevention as part of the overhaul of the healthcare system.

Employers and insurers are now changing their perspective on prevention and the need to drive consumers to healthier lifestyles. They have tried the "carrot" approach for many years, offering incentives to improve lifestyles. They now believe that the "stick" may be more effective in generating change.

Recent studies by Vimo of Mountain View, California, project that CDHPs could cover as many as 50 million individuals by 2010. This research also indicates that many of the HSA accounts that are partnered with these plans will be underfunded in the early years. Having said that, the study indicates that there could already be almost $1 billion collectively in these accounts. Vimo notes that the purpose of these accounts is not to avoid spending money on healthcare but to do so more efficiently. Prevention and wellness are clearly important tools in retaining funds both for today and for the future.

Whether immediate or long-term in nature, there are clearly going to be more tools available to support wellness and prevention on all levels. An interesting dynamic is that common ground could actually be built between the employer and employee in the process. It is clear that a healthier future benefits both groups, and this could be the subject to bring them together. This could be a positive benefit of the process and would revive employers' hopes that there are controls that are realistic and functional.

A number of new tools are available to insurers, employers, and consumers to aid in their newfound interest in prevention and wellness. Some of these are simple information sites designed to use education as a tool to increase knowledge and compliance with healthy activities and lifestyles. Others are integrated into employer and insurance programs and are designed to be more aggressive wellness solutions. Both types use multiple delivery formats and interactive tools.

HealthMedia, located in Ann Arbor, Michigan, is a leader in online prevention and wellness systems offered through employers, providers, and health plans across the country. The company's tagline states that it is "revolutionizing behavioral change." Its systems work to replicate or supplement a traditional nurse counseling telephone session through the use of interactive online communications. The program is scalable and virtually any size employer or group can use the Web-based intervention systems.

HealthMedia's system is designed for multiple applications, from prevention to disease management to behavioral health to medication compliance. Each major area has a unique program and set of tools used to drive change. The programs are designed to impact both short- and long-term costs by increasing the contact points and information relevant to consumer needs. The Web-based delivery mechanism, combined with the program's scalability, makes the program effective across a wide range of needs and budgets.

These systems offer tools that help assess not only a participant's health, but also his or her motivation and confidence in order to identify barriers that might prohibit behavioral change. The program then develops a customized plan that establishes an emotional connection to the participant. This plan follows proven clinical and behavioral change guidelines and generates quantifiable outcome measurements.

A broad series of online intervention products are available that focus on specific categories, including health and wellness, disease management, medication compliance and behavioral health. They offer a medical library in a variety of formats, including some information delivered through podcasts. All programs include goal setting and coaching to help participants work toward specific goals. The program is unique as it gives the same importance and intensity to wellness as to disease management. The program is offered in multilingual formats for use by the expanding ethnic populations in America.

HealthMedia has conducted extensive studies and clinical work showing that its programs reduce costs through better utilization and health. The programs have been featured in a number of targeted clinical studies for the measurable outcomes and success stories and have won leadership awards from several national organizations for their innovative tools and approaches. HealthMedia's tools show potential to help control the future costs of care and educate consumers to improve and manage their own health.

20 The Shift of Financial Power

The scenario we are painting in *Healthcare Tsunami* is an interesting one from a number of perspectives. First, it will change the way care is delivered in this country. It will then bring about true consumerism in the healthcare industry, not just the watered-down version in which consumers want more and better choices. Finally, it will impact costs as consumers become more responsible in purchasing services and using their limited dollars.

While the tsunami may not reach all aspects of healthcare and may not have direct impact on those individuals who use the most services, it is likely to change the perspective of many and may help at least put social pressure on those who use extensive care and services unnecessarily. If the tsunami truly shows that it can change the system, the government may even step in and force users to behave more like consumers. All of this will cause a significant change in who has the financial power within the varying market segments discussed in this book.

Within the current marketplace, three players hold the financial power in the healthcare process—the employer that funds the care, the insurer that provides the funding structure, and the provider that delivers the services. The consumer's role has been relatively minor in the current setting, as consumers generally pay less than 30% of the cost of their care. These three groups have exchanged funds for many years and have become accustomed to the flow of that cash through their systems.

Think now what will happen if HSAs become a significant factor in the industry. The employer will still provide monies, in part. The process of change, though, is about redirecting the financial responsibility of healthcare from the employer to the employee. Consumers will assume a greater percentage of financing and more direct control over the funds they hold. While employers may continue to be players in the process, they will not carry the financial clout they once did. Consumers will then occupy that role.

The flip side of this discussion is that employers will lose some of the financial clout they had with both the providers and insurers. With more of the financial power moving to consumers who will make related decisions, employers may not play the role they once did in the process. Most employers may be happy to rid themselves of this responsibility. In fact, some employers may drop the responsibility completely by giving their employees a salary adjustment to seek their own individual coverage in the commercial market.

Providers are also likely to see the financial impact of change through, for example, less duplication of testing and services, delays in care to conserve monies, and more questions about the need for testing. Providers will feel the squeeze and will have to create different models of delivery to meet consumer cost needs. They may have to streamline operations and use a more regional approach for services they cannot offer on a cost-competitive basis locally.

Another opportunity for providers may be to aggressively pursue the wellness and prevention market. Since wellness investments are appearing to become good investments for all players, a sharp provider has an opportunity to recoup some lost revenues. Recent studies show that holders of HSAs are already spending more on prevention than they did when they had traditional coverage.

In the middle of these two groups is the insurance industry, which will also likely lose some of its financial clout as the change plays out. Since consumers are moving to HDHPs, the premium dollars generated will not be what they have been. This, combined with the loss of dollars placed in HSAs, will reduce the cash flow of insurers and change their base financial reserves. While the success of consumerism may not necessarily impact the bottom line of insurers, it does have the potential to reduce rates and further reduce cash flow within these organizations. The insurance industry significantly benefits from the value of this cash moving through its business. Competitive pressures arising from increasing deductibles could also put stress on the insurers.

The loss of cash flow is a key factor in the insurance industry's movement to gain bank charters. If insurers can retain some of the dollars from HSAs, they will have the power of the cash reserves they create. For years, insurers have been savvy investors and have made money investing their premium dollar holdings in reserve and in liquid accounts. This may be an essential part of the future for many of those insurers that may be heavily impacted by the changing marketplace for insurance coverage.

As noted in the previous chapter, a recent study indicates that there could already be almost $1 billion in HSAs. The projected growth in these accounts could more than triple by 2010. This is a tremendous shift in financial power and responsibility to consumers. They will truly have greater control over their futures in ways related to both their healthcare expenditures and their financial futures.

Remember again that the current rules governing these accounts allow consumers to retain and build funds not used for medical costs from year to year. They also have the ability to perform a one-time rollover from a qualified retirement account to their HSA. This is especially important in the early years of the accounts. Current data indicate an average balance in these accounts of just under $1,200, with most HDHPs working with deductibles of $1,500 or, more commonly, $2,500. So, the accounts are currently underfunded if a true need were to arise. A one-time rollover contribution of $2,850 per individual and $5,500 per family to the account could be the solution.

As the years go by, these accounts will build in value. Remember that 85% of consumers spend less than $500 annually on healthcare. This means that accounts should grow relatively quickly within the next 5 to 10 years. Other legislative changes may also allow further funding of these accounts to speed the transition to consumerism, as well as serving as investment opportunities for players battling to become leaders in these accounts. This will build another source of wealth for many young and healthy consumers who are already showing signs that they will take better care of themselves in the process.

We believe this future offers many opportunities for key players to be partners with consumers in building their health and wealth. These partners will again use education and a variety of tools to show consumers how to best use this new power to build stable, long-term financial futures. This will create new business relationships in the new consumerism following the tsunami.

21 Branding in the New Era of Healthcare Consumerism

As healthcare consumerism tips into mainstream acceptance, businesses that acknowledge the trend and modify their marketing will prosper. Those who ignore the new power of the emerging consumer will face a loss of market share. A powerful tool to help any company ride the wave to success, rather than being driven under, is branding.

Smart businesspeople have embraced the concept of branding since commerce began thousands of years ago. More recently, the concept of branding has become trendy. It is common to pick up any business publication and find the words *brand* and *branding* liberally used, often with contradictory meanings. Although the attention paid to the concept of branding has been positive, the misuse of the term has created confusion. In this chapter, we will explain the basic foundations of branding and how a company can maxi mize its marketing to attract new customers while building bullet-proof customer loyalty.

A brand is not a logo or an ad. Branding is not creating a new name or identity. A brand (noun) is a tangible product or service and the emotional feelings that are associated with the product. Branding (verb) is carefully crafting what you offer and managing the feelings and expectations of your customers.

Many cognitive scientists believe that up to 95% of all behavior is unconscious. Emotions have far more impact on our decision-making process than does logic alone. Branding isn't, and never was, just about building a better mousetrap. If we made our purchases based upon logic and material value alone, the world would be a very different place.

The benefits of understanding and managing a brand are numerous. Companies that manage their brands not only have greater positive word-of-mouth advertising, they enjoy greater customer loyalty and higher profitability. The return on branding is not just about generating positive feelings; the payoff is something that can be taken to the bank.

Before we review the principals of branding, it is important to understand a few key definitions.

Marketing: The total process of imagining, planning, and implementing business activities intended to bring together buyers and sellers for the mutually advantageous exchange of products or services.

Brand: (noun) A product or service and the sum total of feelings and expectations of the marketplace for that product or service.

Branding: (verb) Managing the brand for maximum loyalty and profitability.

Advertising: Paid communications (media and creative) designed to influence a specific target audience.

"It's a rare generic defect. To put it bluntly, you have no brand loyalty."

Public Relations: The relationship between an organization and its various "publics" and its effort to influence positive publicity and awareness.

Sales: The process of preparing and interacting with current and prospective customers to facilitate the immediate transfer of goods and/or services.

Alegent Health, a Nebraska-based not-for-profit healthcare system, pioneered a consumer-driven healthcare plan for its employees in 2005. The plan and programs are well documented and can serve as tangible examples of how consumer healthcare branding can drive participation and positive cost savings while improving the health of participants. We will refer to Alegent and its program throughout this chapter to help make branding theory more concrete.

Branding begins with attitude. As healthcare consumerism grows, it will require a shift in how consumers think about and engage in healthcare consumption. It will also require a shift in the basic philosophy of many business leaders, some of whom seem to be in denial that any change will occur. Many consumers, providers, and insurers are uncomfortable with this power shift. Education will be key in selling across marketing channels, reducing anxiety, and creating adoption. Pricing transparency is just one proof point of this idea.

Perceptions are reality. To most healthcare providers, quality is measured by the efficiency of the process and the ultimate health-related outcome. In the absence of quantifiable data proving value, consumers will fall back upon their experience to drive their individual rating of value. To consumers, a quality healthcare outcome may depend upon how they were treated. In short, most consumers want to feel cared about, not just cared for. This will require a shift at a basic level for most providers. Except for their relationship with a primary care physician, most consumers currently consider providers to be a commodity. As with other services and products, those providers who are able to cater to customers as individuals, while at the same time making them feel special and valued, will gain market share.

The defining attitudinal moment for Alegent's CEO, Wayne Sensor, came during a meeting with a prominent business leader. To begin building bridges with the business community, Sensor met with leaders to gain perspective. In one meeting, Sensor was asked, "What are you doing with your own workforce to engage them as consumers?" At that point Sensor realized that Alegent needed to take a leadership role to help the ailing system it was part of. By shifting payment responsibilities from patients to insurers, the incentive for patients to analyze the value of care they receive had all but disappeared. Adding to the problem, there was virtually no way for consumers to predict cost in measuring the value they receive.

Branding is strategic thinking. If a company is not focused on its basic vision, it is not maximizing its resources. There are two basic strategic components to branding. The first is brand vision. The vision of any organization is the reason it exists and the passion that drives its people to succeed. Although a vision must include a value proposition for the customer, it should also include a higher purpose. That purpose has usually been, or should be, defined by the founders and/or leaders of the organization. That vision is a private statement of purpose and should drive all major business decisions.

Alegent adopted a new brand vision and titled it the "Quality Revolution." At the heart of the brand vision is a plan to put consumers at the center of the healthcare equation by empowering them to take charge of their own healthcare and make better, more informed decisions.

The other strategic component of branding is brand position. If vision is the internal driving force, then positioning is the external driving force. It is how a company wants to be seen and valued by its customers. The brand position is a public face. It relates directly to the vision and comprises a statement of value for customers.

Understanding that education would play a vital role in the success of its new initiative, Alegent initiated the development of a brand position for its program, which featured a consumer-focused benefit platform. Alegent rolled out its program, titled "Next Generation Health," in a variety of formats, all focused on how the program benefits the participant.

One way to consider any business model and the interplay of features and emotions is through the levels of brand associations. The foundation of any product or service is the features or processes that it provides. These represent the day-to-day deliverables of the product or service; they must be delivered to provide value. Features or attributes represent the component of a product or service that is easiest to deliver and to be imitated or copied by any competitor. Attributes make up the majority of advertising messages, but in reality they are the least meaningful to consumers.

Of greater importance to consumers are the benefits offered by any exchange. These represent the functional or emotional benefits being provided by a product or service.

At the top levels of brand associations are beliefs and values. These represent the emotional, cultural, and spiritual values that are provided when a customer buys a product or service from any company. These values are the most meaningful to consumers and are the hardest to imitate.

Quick, what do you think of when you read the word *Volvo*? Most people will respond "safety." Over the years, Volvo has worked very hard to own the value of safety. On the bottom level of Volvo's brand associations is the company's vehicles and dealer network. The attributes include the cars themselves and their features. At the benefit level, Volvo offers improved personal and family protection should the car be involved in an accident. At the top level of Volvo's brand associations is safety.

When communicated, beliefs and values are much more engaging than the attributes or benefits of any product could ever be. One of Volvo's recent campaigns is "Who Would You Give a Volvo To?" This is a great example of positioning to the emotional values of a product. Volvo is not selling the attributes of its vehicles, it is selling the fact that if you care about your family, and you want to keep them safe, you will drive a Volvo. This is a very powerful message.

Recognizing that cost is a vital component of determining value, Alegent pioneered a unique, patent-pending online tool that provides consumers with information on projected costs they will incur for nearly 500 common treatments and procedures, along with their out-of-pocket responsibility. All estimates are personally relevant, as they are based upon a consumer's particular health plan or financial situation.

Current customers are the lifeblood of any company. It takes 7 to 10 times as much investment to get a new customer as it does to keep a current one. In the healthcare industry, new customer, or patient, acquisition is even more expensive. As the first step in any branding process, we first recommend shoring up a company's relationship with its existing customers. We ask a series of important operational questions: Do you have a method of customer feedback? Are you aware of any issues your customers have with you? What are your customer touchpoints, and are you working toward a positive experience in every customer encounter? Do you understand how your customers judge value? Are you driving positive word of mouth? What are the inherent brand promises you make, and are you fulfilling them? Who are your competitors and what value do they offer? The answers to these questions point to solid tactical measures necessary to bolster customer relationships.

As women continue to evolve as the primary decision makers regarding their family's healthcare, it becomes more important than ever to understand their needs and wants. As reported in *Fast Company* (Nov. 2003), women control or influence more than 80% of purchases in the United States, a total of about $3.5 trillion every year. As discussed earlier, many of the decision-making criteria are based upon emotional characteristics such as relationships and what the service does for the consumers personally and for their families. In general, lists or statistics alone will not motivate this market to action. Careful and considered attention must be devoted to the real motivating factors that will cause women to respond. For example, to help treat some of the most common ailments facing children and families, Alegent opened Quick Care clinics in Hy-Vee food stores. These facilities offer a convenient, patient-friendly atmosphere.

A key component to successful branding will involve mass customization. According to *Wikipedia*, mass customization is "a business technique that allows any customer to buy a product or service that has been pre-designed (customized) to fit a customer's exact needs." In short, mass customization provides the efficiency of mass production with the uniqueness of customization.

In a marketplace of adequate supply and consumer choice, understanding and delivering a mass customized service or product is vital. As we all face increased demands on our time and other resources, we will look toward solutions that cater to us as individuals while respecting our time and providing value. As consumers become free to choose where and when they will receive their care, they will base their choices on providers that focus on them.

An example of mass customization lies in the potential value of electronic medical record (EMR) systems. In work with consumers, we have found that few recognize the value of EMR. In fact, most feel that EMR is simply a cost of doing business and that all providers already have some form of EMR in place. Where EMR may play to consumers is through its ability to track personal information. Cataloging and recalling personal information for every patient could provide great assistance in helping patients feel valued.

Many patients complain that providers do not review their charts prior to an appointment. How would that perception change if EMR were used to remind the doctor of the name of a patient's child or some personal anecdote from his or her last visit? Enabling a database to help cue personal information is an example of mass customization and may play an important role in helping customers (patients) feel cared for during their visit.

Furthermore, EMR systems help demonstrate something else that is closely monitored by patients—their time. If a patient switches providers, he or she can simply have his or her medical records transferred to the new provider. Patients will no longer need to arrive 15 to 20 minutes early to fill out a plethora of forms. In addition, patients will not have to use the doctor's valuable time explaining their medical history. The doctor will have this information at his or her fingertips, along with a complete history of diagnoses, tests, treatments, and prescriptions.

22 How to Reach the New Consumer

We believe that reaching the new healthcare consumer will be quite similar to reaching any other consumer group in society today. The key is to identify the group, understand the members' behavior and habits, and develop strategies that reach them in ways that are both efficient and meaningful. This has been the standard approach to consumer marketing for some time. The biggest challenge in this environment is that it is new ground and not a great deal is known about the true healthcare consumer.

Some early research indicates that the true healthcare consumer, one who is knowledgeable and places major importance on costs in his or her selection of care, is relatively rare. It is thought that less than 10% of privately covered individuals fall into this category. More are showing some level of cost sensitivity in their selection and decision-making processes. We expect that these groups will increase in number as the tsunami moves through society, and more consumers are spending their own dollars.

Like the marketing of other products, marketing health services after the tsunami will be a moving target. Just when you think you understand consumers, their needs will change. Good marketers will be students of these new consumers, observing their behavior and the patterns of change that occur as they move through different levels of knowledge and experience. We believe there are starting points that are safe to assume as marketers in this new era.

Consumers in the early stages of the transition will likely be younger, most commonly under age 45. The most interested consumers will be even younger than that. Females may prove to be the most receptive audience, especially those with children. They are more frequent users of services and appear to be the primary healthcare decision makers.

We believe that communicating with this new consumer will be rather simple. The newly found incentive to be better consumers is financial in nature and is likely to generate interest by the group in learning more. Existing evidence already shows this to be true. Messages targeting value and education should be strong tools in reaching these consumers.

Work completed by The Leede Research Group in the past two years consistently indicates that consumers and even employers have not formed important opinions that are critical in the consumer environment. We find that few respondents can name players when asked about attributes such as concerned about costs, future cost controls, a partner in controlling costs, value for the healthcare dollar, and other attributes that would be seen in industries that are consumer-driven. This lack of positioning is a real opportunity for the early players in the provider category.

We believe that providers and insurers should act now to position themselves as partners with consumers in their short- and long-term goals. Both groups should be seen as part of the solution to the healthcare crisis, and working to both control costs and offer value. These are new and unoccupied positions in consumer minds and ones that can become dominant.

Those who are seen by new healthcare consumers as partners in their physical and financial health will have a significant advantage over their competitors. They will be able to create valued brands that consumers respect. Furthermore, they will be seen as controlling costs and perceived as truly having the best interests of the customer in mind, thus building strong, loyal relationships with consumers. This is key to generating the word-of-mouth advertising that can be so valuable in this segment. This process can create brand advocates who will expand the reach and contact of that brand.

Our past research indicates that providers and insurers must be careful in the way they communicate with consumers. Consumers are skeptical that anyone can or even wants to deal with the issue of rising healthcare costs. Some also believe that much of healthcare marketing is bragging or telling consumers what they want to hear. Consumers, in the end, distrust the message and the way it is delivered.

Communications should speak directly to individual patients in a way that respects them and communicates on their level. These should be discussions *with* patients, not lectures *to* patients. Providers must be careful not to talk down to them and avoid telling them what they should or should not know. Providers should not preach to patients about what they

"I can't identify emotionally with any brand of anything..."

should or should not do, but simply create a two-person dialogue that communicates how the provider is going to help the patient through this new and exciting opportunity.

The most effective advertising messages are not feature or benefit focused. Advertising that motivates through emotion provides the highest return on investment. Companies that invest in quality message strategies will gain a greater share of the market and do it faster than their competition. This will be even more important as more dollars are poured into advertising. As consumers become bombarded, it will be more difficult for any one company to stand out from the crowd. Consumers will tune out messages that fail to promise meaningful value to them personally.

New marketing methods should seek to educate new consumers. They need to understand their plan design and recognize basic coverage terminology, including the true meaning of *deductible*, *out-of-pocket expense*, *co-pay,* and other terms that they will encounter on a regular basis. Consumers need to understand the role of an HSA in combination with an HDHP. They need to know they can now roll over funds from their IRA to support the early years of the plan. They need to understand how to track their medical usage and keep accurate records of their expenses, not only for immediate reimbursement, but also for possible tax audits.

Teaching consumers to better understand how the healthcare system works and how they can make better decisions in their selection of care, testing, and treatment will be invaluable. Price is a new concept in this segment, and consumers will need to be taught that price is not always cost. Knowing the difference between price and cost is essential. Messages should teach consumers that utilization is a factor, and that while unit pricing is important if one provider achieves the same outcome in fewer visits, the actual cost may be lower even though the unit pricing is higher. Providers will succeed if they give consumers resources that they can use on their own to educate themselves and become better consumers, all the time reinforcing the reasons it is important to do so.

As the tsunami sweeps away the current model of healthcare, a new, consumer-based version of healthcare marketing is emerging. Those that survive and gain the largest share will know that success is not just about what people think, but how they feel. What's currently perceived as unimportant or frivolous will attract new attention and resources. Respecting patients, making them comfortable, and catering to them on a personal level will take on new importance. In addition, facilities will continue to evolve. Hospitals and clinics will look and feel more welcoming. The stainless steel and ceramic tile environments will be replaced with warm, comfortable, and inviting settings.

"I'm torn between brand loyalty & changing trends in the consumer experience."

Customer experience will take on a new role after the tsunami. While delivery of quality care is always important, the true differentiator will be the experience customers have in their use of services. Providing a unique experience that exceeds consumers' expectations will generate positive word of mouth and will convert customers into advocates. This has always been important, but it will play a more critical role in future success.

When we consider other consumer-based brands, the primary drivers for determining loyalty are, in order of importance, high quality and/or reliability and performance. Secondary drivers include familiarity, the price/value relationship, fitting the consumer's personality, and effectively solving the consumer's problems.

As prices become more transparent, some consumers will base their choice on price. This is consistent with other models, as this group refuses to consider the service as any more than a commodity and will make up about 4–8% of the population. The majority will consider price but evaluate their purchase and loyalty on a much broader scale. This is the concept of value.

Let's consider this and how these loyalty indicators relate to healthcare. First, quality. When asked for his or her definition of quality, a physician will most likely cite a dedication to efficient diagnosis and treatment. This is natural, understandable, and desirable. But consumers measure quality by completely different sets of standards. What is most important to patients is the value they receive from their perspective, which, right or wrong, may not include the efficiency of their care.

To the average consumer, quality is not based exclusively on health outcomes. Ask any patient today about a positive healthcare experience, and he or she is unlikely to say the physician was extremely efficient in his or her diagnosis and treatment. Rather, people will respond that their healthcare provider made them feel special, that they were listened to, valued, and cared about—by one who knew their children's names and treated them with concern and caring.

If the real deliverable is health, why don't consumers place more importance on the efficiency of their care and the medical quality of their outcomes? Although consumers may have loyalty to a particular primary care physician or a nostalgic attachment to a hospital, they really don't know how to evaluate effective care. In the absence of any simple measurement, consumers will fall back to personal, anecdotal experiences to judge quality. A study by the AMA cited "bedside manner" as a major determinant in patients defining the quality of their physician. As consumers become more empowered to make their healthcare decisions, the sum total of all consumer touch points will have as much power to drive brand preference as the medical quality of care.

We believe that over time consumers will become more educated, more medically literate, and better able to make more informed decisions about their quality of care. This process will be generated through sites run both by the government and private business that will allow for the comparison of quality through accepted standards such as the CAHPS surveys and other national tools. This may move the perspective of quality in the direction of the provider and help providers better understand consumers and their needs. This process will take time, though.

Consumers' acceptance and tolerance for substandard service will change. What was acceptable when someone else was paying the bills may not be acceptable when they are paying directly. This may not always be obvious, as consumers may simply find alternative providers, such as retail or nontraditional clinics, to fill service needs that they have had issues with in the past. By the time the traditional providers recognize the loss, it may be too late to regain the consumers' confidence. The time to act is now before the tsunami hits.

We are not implying that the new market will tolerate gross negligence. If a provider is providing substandard care, the market will acknowledge the discrepancy and react accordingly. Proof is the emergence of a few new providers who are able to command premium prices while offering quality care and honoring the consumer model.

We believe the new healthcare consumers will include several different groups that behave differently according to their individual needs and situations. The key to success is found in understanding the key groups and identifying the messages that might motivate their behavior and secure their loyalty. These will be different for each of the key players in the new healthcare environment. For the purposes of this chapter, we will discuss the opportunities for insurers, providers, and retailers.

Some general target groups will remain consistent across all three players. We believe that these groups are generally segmented by age, by contact points, and by experience in the healthcare system. The groupings are based on the consumers' current experience and behavior, and these groups could change after the tsunami begins to seriously impact behavior. The following are what we see as the key target populations:

65 and Older Consumers: Members of this group are considered the primary users of health services. They are also generally on government coverage with some form of supplemental insurance, which means the group is less likely to be a part of the consumerism movement. But these individuals will be impacted by consumerism, depending upon the action taken by government in the process. This segment's health needs tend to be more significant, and Medicare coverage generally gives them more flexibility and choice in the providers and services they use.

This group is currently being marketed to through traditional channels in print and media. The messages are generally those of quality, advanced technology, availability of specialists and strong outcomes. This group's members are more traditional patients, and therefore they tend to evaluate the system based on years of experience. They have a long-standing relationship with their primary care physician of probably more than 15 years. They trust this physician and rely on their relationship to guide them to needed services.

This group is not likely to change doctors unless forced. They are highly satisfied and would generally use the same network and facilities they have used for the past 5 to 10 years. While they are relatively easy to contact and reach, it is challenging to influence or change their behavior, based on a long history of personal experience. To successfully change selection behavior with this group, a marketer must find access points that might be outside these individuals' primary relationships and experience, such as health screenings or education programs that can help them improve their health and quality of life.

While the members of this group are less concerned about cost in their decision making, we believe they can still be motivated by a message of value. They are generally no longer working and may be attempting to extend their resources. They are concerned about outcomes and the personal care they receive during the process, but generally want to develop long-term relationships with providers they feel care about their needs and value their business.

35- to 65- Year-Old Consumers: This midrange group shares characteristics with their younger and older counterparts. These individuals will generally be on some type of commercial insurance plan, whether provided by an employer or purchased individually. The younger members of this group may be on HSAs and HDHPs and will demonstrate consumerism tendencies. They will become educated and work to understand how to make better healthcare decisions. Even some of the older members of the group may be on HDHPs because employers have forced them to adopt such plans in order to continue coverage.

The older members of this group may decide that they are close enough to Medicare age that they do not have to learn to be good consumers. They may coast through the final years to age 65 and behave much as they always have. They also have long-standing relationships with a primary care physician and will likely rely on his or her recommendations for the use of services and access to specialists. Because they are still likely to be working, changes in coverage may force them to evaluate their relationships and lead to forced change if their coverage requires it. Those with financial resources may choose to keep long-standing relationships and will pay higher out-of-pocket costs to do so.

The members of this group have moderate experience with the healthcare delivery system. They have gained experience from contact in both their care and that of their children. Their children have grown and some are empty-nesters. They have disposable income, thus representing a sound opportunity for marketers in all related categories. They are planning both their financial and health-related futures and may be receptive to coverage for long-term care. Prevention and wellness are likely to be another opportunity as these individuals come to understand that their use of health services will likely increase. Living healthily could be a key message, as it will address their financial and physical quality of life in the future.

This is a mixed group from a media standpoint and will reflect different opportunities among both younger and older counterparts. They are likely still users of many of the traditional media, including newspapers and magazines, but are also likely to be Web savvy and use online tools in the management of their health and information gathering. They may not be a part of online communities but can be reached through online tools and resources. Creating portals with information of value to them could be a way to attract this group.

Under-35 Consumers: This group will be the most unique of those in the new healthcare environment. Our existing research in several industries has documented that the members of this group are more challenging than their older counterparts. We find they are very brand-oriented. They seek out national and regional brands and identify with them more than with local or small operations. This appears to be based on a desire to have a consistent experience wherever they may choose to go. Mobility is a factor in this attitude because they tend to travel more frequently and change both jobs and residences more often. Interestingly, these consumers are actually less brand loyal than the older demographics.

These younger consumers will play an important role in the future of healthcare delivery and the success of a variety of new ventures born after the tsunami hits U.S. business. They are already having a serious impact on traditional providers and their services, as they are the dominant users of walk-in services and are leading the drive toward retail clinics—with an even more pronounced effect if there are children in the household. They will likely be the primary focus as the retail clinics and the other new models that might evolve from the process look for new products, services, and opportunities.

They may also play a subtler role in the new healthcare environment after the tsunami—one of teacher. Remember that a good deal of healthcare selection and decision making is based on word-of-mouth discussion with friends and family. As members of this younger population experience the new healthcare, they are likely to talk to others about it. This will assist the change process by promoting positive experience with new alternatives. Also remember that members of this group are likely to be caring for older relatives at some point in their lives and will likely use services they prefer and have experience with.

The under-35 population appears to offer the greatest opportunity for providers, because they have a lower likelihood of existing relationships and are also more motivated by convenience. While this group represents a significant opportunity, it may be the most challenging of the three groups to reach and influence. These consumers tend not to follow traditional media in the same way as the older population, generally reading less printed material. They tend not to listen to traditional radio, choosing instead to use satellite radio or podcasts to target their specific interests.

Members of this group are most receptive to online communications, but their use may be different than that of their slightly older counterparts. While both groups use the Web to search for information, this practice is much more ingrained in the younger consumer's everyday lives. They are likely to be part of online communities and use blogs to get the type of information that most interests them. They are computer savvy and their children will be as well, creating new marketing opportunities outside the traditional mass media used in healthcare. Viral marketing can be an effective tool in reaching this group.

Employers: While much of this book discusses the shifting of responsibility for healthcare spending from the employer to the employee, we estimate that employers will still provide more than half the coverage for citizens of the United States after the tsunami. Therefore, this is an influential group that should not be overlooked. Employers still have significant potential for steerage within the system and are a direct contact point to reach consumers with education and marketing messages.

Employers have commonly been a forgotten group in healthcare marketing. The future success of some provider systems may become more dependent upon the steerage influences that can be offered by employers, either through direct contracting or through plan development and networks. This may become more important as some consumer business is lost to the retail providers and nontraditional offerings, thus squeezing bottom lines and leaving unused capacity.

We believe the employer population will continue to play an important role in both the change in the healthcare system and the speed at which the tsunami moves through the economy. The faster employers shift cost burdens to employees, the more rapid the change will be. Marketers will have some challenges in communicating with employers because of their past experience and the current perceptions about the industries of both insurance and providers.

Our research indicates that employers' frustration with current trends in cost has led them to, in some ways, shut down from a communication standpoint. They are not as receptive as they once were to ideas and information regarding cost-saving tools and other programs designed to minimize cost increases. They believe that no one is going to help them, including employees. The movement to HDHPs is a tool to make employees responsible for their own fate and simplify the process for the employer.

Opportunities still clearly exist to reach employers, but it may take more time and resources to do so. They may not be receptive to traditional mass marketing messages because of their frustration. The good news is that many of the messages that would be important to consumers are also important to the employer because they now share a more common cost perspective. When supplemented with direct marketing materials and personal contact through a variety of sales and marketing activities, showing employers that providers and insurers want to partner with them and their employees could be an effective approach in the future.

Change in the perspective of consumers, as it relates to healthcare, will open a whole new arena of marketing opportunities for providers, retailers, financial institutions, and anyone who wants to work to attract dollars from consumers. Healthcare marketing has always had a unique perspective in that providers generally did not have to address issues such as price, cost, or value in their marketing. The industry sought to market the high-quality care it provided in a number of different settings. In the early days of healthcare marketing, this was effective as there were generally notable differences in the quality of care between some providers.

In today's environment, the use of quality as a key differentiator between providers is almost impossible. Most healthcare users perceive high quality among all providers and are satisfied with the care they have received. There is no longer enough difference between providers to justify a dominant position based on quality. The use of quality in healthcare marketing is likely to continue, however, because it is so ingrained into the system, but the key to future success is to find other points of differentiation. The message used must be unique and important to consumers. Finding this message will allow providers to position themselves uniquely in their market and work to generate increased market share.

We believe there will be opportunities to do this in the days after the tsunami. With consumers spending their own dollars, there are a number of positions that can be taken in light of their newfound responsibility. The core position involves being seen as a partner in meeting their needs and as a solution to their problems, especially for providers and insurers. Consumers will be in new and uncharted territory, seeking help to understand what they should do. A player could create a strong bond with consumers by helping them in that process.

Being a partner means that a provider, insurer, or retailer will help consumers be healthy and make better decisions related to their healthcare and the use of related services. This is an education-based marketing position that seeks to provide tools to inform consumers and give them the information they need to make better choices in the future. The goal is to demonstrate how they can save money and reduce future costs in both short- and long-term environments.

The Leede Research Group has used positioning research techniques in its work since the early 1980s. Positioning is a concept developed and popularized by the 1976 book *Positioning:The Battle for Your Mind,* by agency executives Trout and Ries. They indicated that because we live in an overcommunicated society, our minds cannot hold on to all the information. Because of that, our minds begin to work a lot like a computer and build files, or what they call ladders. For a simple demonstration of this, take out a piece of paper and a pencil. Set down the book and jot down as many brand names of televisions as you can. Do this in your head if you wish.

How many did you list? The original concept says that in any category that is not of direct interest or importance to consumers, he or she will generally name between three and seven brands. How did you do? Did you have Sony, Zenith, or Hitachi in your top three? These would be the traditional leaders on the ladder called Television, which is represented by more than 200 brands in today's market.

We have found that the ladders within the healthcare industry tend to segment into two major categories. The first relates to specific product or service offerings. The second relates to specific attributes associated with the major category, or the more soft marketing elements that are used in the category, such as quality, selection, ease of doing business, advanced technology, and others.

We have used positioning in our healthcare research and tracked the changes in consumer and employer positioning of key service and attributes. We find that a number of new ladders have not been formed in the minds of these groups, but could represent a significant opportunity for those who develop and occupy them. Results of recent work indicate that over half the respondents to healthcare positioning surveys cannot name providers for positions such as: working to control future costs, a partner in education, a leader in prevention and wellness, and best value for the dollar. These will all be valuable positions in the days after the tsunami.

New positions will also develop around cost. The market might not be ready for true price-point marketing, which is a factor in some consumer categories. Historically, some providers attempted to market low price to consumers in the mid to late 1980s. These attempts were not well received by consumers, who said they did not want to use the "cheapest" hospital in town for the care of their loved ones. This was during the time of the third-party payer, so price was not important to these consumers.

The new price-point marketing may be more about efficiency and value than about price. The effective marketing message will be about good value for the dollar spent. It may also play on the fact that the true cost of healthcare is not just about the unit price of services. It is about the total utilization, services used, and visits required during an episode of care. Providers may be able to identify that they offer strong value with a lower total cost per episode.

We believe that a message of value is one that can resonate across all the populations discussed in this chapter. While the older populations may be less motivated by consumer experience, they are still consumers. Although they may not be spending their own dollars, they will understand that others are. They will also understand that the decisions younger consumers make are based on sound investigation and they may seek the same providers used by younger family members. The value message could be effective across all groups and would certainly be of interest to the employer, who is still covering the bulk of care.

23 Closing Thoughts

The healthcare system in America simply cannot continue under existing conditions. To do so would be virtually impossible. Simple math shows that by 2020 the cost of healthcare will eventually exceed our personal income. Whether costs are paid by employers, the government, or consumers, we know that this cannot occur. How did we reach a point where healthcare spending went from only 7% of personal income in the 1920s to possibly 100% in just 100 years?

Consumerism in healthcare is the result of a natural progression of the marketplace that should have happened many years ago. A strange set of circumstances created the environment we have today, and the market is trying to find a balance under which it can function effectively. This is not without challenges, and there will be many bumps in the road before we reach an ultimate solution.

A very large percentage of healthcare spending is generated by a relatively small percentage of consumers, generally those who have major issues or chronic conditions. We predict that these individuals will not be immediately impacted by the tsunami. Therefore, change in the healthcare industry will take much longer to accomplish. The hope is that the positive impact of consumerism will eventually reach all segments and result in smarter consumers, cost reductions, and improved quality of care and service. The question becomes whether it can stem the upward-spiraling costs of care in time to save the system.

Consumerism will address only a minor portion of the total spending on healthcare, but it will still involve billions of dollars changing hands. Smart, young consumers will find that they have new tools to manage both their health and financial futures. We will see new incentives for prevention and wellness to improve overall health, while at the same time improving overall wealth. Solving a part of the healthcare dilemma may also have an influence on the Social Security system, as consumers find new ways to create funding for retirement.

The transfer of wealth will be empowering to some, yet daunting to others. Where monies were sitting in the reserves of health insurers or in the accounts of providers, consumers will now have control of some of these dollars. This will create new wealth, new spending, new industries, and new players in a variety of categories from healthcare to retail to financial services.

Some current players will feel the pain of change. None of us like change until it is completed and we see the benefits. Change is not without its victims. Some businesses will fail because they cannot adapt to the new model. We may see that we have built too much healthcare capacity in this country, and the consumer model will squeeze out players that cannot meet consumer needs and compensate for the reduced volume that better spending creates.

Putting dollars for healthcare in the hands of the people who spend them will not be without its horror stories. Some people will undoubtedly choose wealth over health, which will lead to short- and long-term health issues. This will happen regardless of how well we design the systems to reward preventive care and how well we educate consumers. The media will debate the issue and many will say, "I said this would happen." It's human nature and unavoidable.

The reality is that having consumers spend their own dollars makes sense! It has made sense in every other industry in the world and it will make sense in healthcare as well. As American consumers, we vote every day, each time we take out our wallets. We vote for gas stations and grocery stores and retail stores and car dealers. We grant that vote by the dollars we spend, and in that election the winners are those businesses that provide a quality product at a price that meets our budget. We believe that this voting process can be brought to the healthcare equation and can serve to bring that industry in alignment with the needs and budgets of the people.

As we well know, the best voter is an educated voter. Along with this newfound freedom comes responsibility. Consumers of healthcare must become educated. Education will require an investment in both time and dedication and will also require partners who can supply the right tools and information to make better decisions. Consumers will see a financial return in learning and being smarter, and thus be more willing to pay for the education.

Just like going to college after high school increases our income potential down the road, education in healthcare and greater medical literacy will increase our effectiveness in spending our healthcare dollars. Those dollars we do not spend will remain in our accounts and grow. Our medical literacy will extend our lives and decrease mortality rates, creating new opportunities both for existing players and for businesses that might not even be on the drawing board today.

Consumers will come to see the impact of their lifestyles, both from a physical perspective and a financial perspective, which will help change bad habits and improve overall health. It will help reduce the 70% of medical costs that are tied to lifestyle choices that consumers make. Prevention and wellness will find new audiences in consumers who now have a new incentive to be healthy, which will also create new opportunities for business. This newfound wellness will help address many issues related to the younger generation moving into middle age.

How will you respond to life after the tsunami? What will it mean for your business? Will you be crushed by the wave of change or ride it to a new place in the American economy? These are questions that only you can answer and only time will tell. We believe that the future is a bright one for those who see the trends early and understand how to reach the new healthcare consumer.

The good news is that these new consumers will more closely resemble consumers that exist for many other products and services in the United States. If you can partner with them, teach them to use the products and services in the category, and help them save money, everyone will prosper. These new consumers will be hungry for information and ideas that will help them meet their needs.

They will have many new tools to help them in this process. Along with education will come understanding. There will be changes in the way consumers view quality, and they will move from an experience-based perspective to one that is based on both experience and technical quality as measured by tools available to compare quality between providers. These tools will be readily available on the Web and through other direct sources.

In some ways the new healthcare consumers will retain the habits of today. They will look to the relationship they have with their primary care physician as their main connection to the healthcare system. They will rely on that physician's expertise to help them access the specialists, tools, and technology they need for significant health events. They may seek other options to address day-to-day care, and that will likely change the provider model in many settings.

Critics say that we will never be able to fix the current healthcare crisis until we change the fundamental way in which players in the healthcare industry are compensated. They cite a paradox that takes most of the incentive for improvement and change away from the providers: providers are not compensated for making people healthy; they are paid to care for those who are sick. More sick people equals more business; fewer sick people equals lower earnings.

Some systems have attempted to compensate providers for the health of certain patient populations. For example, the capitation system paid providers a fixed amount per employee to care for employees' health needs. The concept was that if the provider could improve the overall health of the capitated patient, it would receive the difference between the payments made and the cost of the care used. These systems fell from favor due in part to increasing costs that made it difficult for providers to project costs over time. There are also CMS experiments cited in this book that share revenues saved in care and treatment.

This paradigm shift may truly be the conversion that needs to take place if we are going to be successful in both improving the health of the population and reducing the significant burden that healthcare costs are putting on our budget and our economy. Consumerism can be a part of this process, as it creates incentives for providers and other groups to help reduce long-term costs. The payment model cannot change with the flip of a switch, but a variety of factors and tools coming together with significant drive can help start the process of change. This transition will require participation by consumers and providers and assistance by the government in terms of fostering an environment of change.

We will soon embark on one of the most comprehensive national surveys of healthcare consumerism ever conducted. It includes a series of surveys directed to each of the key segments that are currently driving the process of change. This study will help identify where we are in the process of change and what will drive the speed of the tsunami in America. We look forward to bringing this information to the marketplace later in the year.

What we have presented in this book represents one of many possible futures. It is built both on a historical foundation and on a set of converging trends that are driving the current process of change. Many variables exist that will impact the size of the change and the influence it will have on business and society.

We hope that this information gets you thinking about the future—a future where change is not only likely, but also inevitable. Think about the current situation, the needs, and the role that you and your business can play in the process. Be a student of the trends. Watch and learn. Make your contributions and seize your opportunities.

Ride the wave.

> About the Authors

Dean Halverson is CEO of The Leede Research Group, a full-service marketing research and information firm, with offices in Wisconsin and Minnesota. Leede Research Group conducts work nationally with a staff of 85 research professionals. The company also partners with a network of professional firms around the world who help to complete projects with international components.

Leede has become a leader in the growing field of healthcare consumerism. Halverson has more than 25 years of marketing and research experience and has managed healthcare-related research projects since 1983. His firm has conducted millions of interviews with consumers of all kinds, working for major companies in health, insurance, financial services and consumer products.

Leede Research Group has a broad range of experience in the healthcare industry, having worked with well over 100 providers in all market sizes, including pharmacy, homecare and hospice organizations, medical manufacturers, health insurers, health plans and even business coalitions. This has given the company a profound understanding of the players and issues that impact healthcare.

Leede Research Group also has extensive experience in financial services, working with banks, credit unions, insurance providers and companies that serve the finance industry. They have seen the movement of the financial industry into secondary industries including investments, brokerage and, most recently, insurance. Now the changes have included the addition of health insurance offerings as well as health savings accounts tied to consumer-driven health plans.

While working with a wide range of industries, Halverson began to see common consumption threads across all industries and how these industries deal with the basic ways in which consumers think and make decisions. He began to understand how the human mind manages the millions of pieces of information it receives from media and advertising, and how that information is used to make decisions. He shares this knowledge as a speaker and educator.

In recent years, Halverson has continuously monitored a set of converging trends that bring together his company's two strongest segments: healthcare and finance. This led to further investigation, which identified factors contributing to a significant change in healthcare and related industries. Thus, the concept of the Healthcare Tsunami was born.

Contributing author, Wayne Glowac, CEO of Glowac, Harris, Madison, Inc., has helped clients achieve uncommon results for more than 25 years. Glowac+Harris is a full-service advertising agency specializing in advertising, public relations and brand consulting and whose experience includes a diverse range of business and consumer clients.

Glowac's previous experience includes founding an award-winning start-up agency, Orion Marketing Group, Inc., in 1991. After a decade of successful operations, Glowac sold Orion, but continued to serve as President. In 2004, with partner, Wayne Harris, Glowac purchased the assets of Orion and reopened as Glowac, Harris, Madison, Inc.

Glowac+Harris has helped companies across business and consumer sectors better understand and manage their most vital asset, their brand. More than just a logo or slogan, branding involves the process of understanding and managing customer expectations and feelings. Glowac has pioneered a number of processes that help clients better understand the key elements which are inherent to successful brand management. The agency's BrandSMART, a branding seminar, has been shared with thousands of companies across the United States. The Glowac+Harris BrandMAP, a best-practice method for defining a brand position, has helped dozens of clients generate above-average return for their marketing investments.

Wayne Glowac was awarded his first ADDY during his first year in business for writing and producing a radio commercial starring his son Preston, then age 6. Since then, Glowac has won a number of awards. His most valued award is the 2004 National Arbor Day Award given to recognize an urban forestry publicity campaign.

Glowac is President of the Marketing Communications Agency Network, an international trade group of advertising agencies. He currently teaches advertising and public relations for the University of Wisconsin-Madison School of Business Extension.

He lives in Cross Plains, Wisconsin with his wife of more than 25 years, Laurie. They have three sons: Preston, Taylor and Connor. Aside from power boating, Glowac enjoys photography, is an avid cyclist and a student of submarine warfare.

Together, Dean Halverson and Wayne Glowac formed WAVE Strategy, LLC. WAVE was created to assist forward-thinking business leaders in healthcare and related fields to thrive during consumer-driven change.

WAVE provides reality-based consumer research, strategic marketing, consulting services and creative brand positioning. Through the process of **W**atching, **A**ssessing, **V**alidating and **E**mploying, WAVE assists business in strategic consumer-driven marketing.

Contact either Dean Halverson or Wayne Glowac at hctsunami.com or wavetrends.com.

> References

1. San Filippo, Joe, CEBS. (2006, December 11) *Nationwide Better Health.* Presentation to the Consumer Directed Health Care Conference, Washington, DC.
2. Davis, Karen, Cathy Schoenbaum, and Ilana Weinbaum. (2007) *Slowing the Growth of U.S. Health Care Expenditures: What are the Options?* New York, NY: The Commonwealth Fund.
3. Meckler, Laura and John Harwood. (2007, June 7) Giuliani Health Proposal Seeks Individual Coverage. *The Wall Street Journal Online.*
4. Thomasson, Melissa. (2003, April 18) "Health Insurance in the United States." EH.Net Encyclopedia, edited by Robert Whaples. URL: http://eh.net/encyclopedia/article/thomasson.insurance.health.us
5. Gorman, Linda, Ph.D. (2006) *The History of Health Care Costs and Health Insurance–A Wisconsin Primer.* Thiensville, WI: Wisconsin Policy Research Institute.

6. Internal Revenue Service. (2007) *Health Savings Accounts and Other Tax-Favored Health Plans* (IRS Publication 969). Washington, DC: Internal Revenue Service.
7. Rogala, Tom. (2007) www.hsasale.com
8. Schuster, Mark, Elizabeth McGlynn, and Robert Book. (1998) How Good is the Quality of Health Care in the United States? The Milbank Quarterly, Volume 76 (No. 4) pp 517-563.
9. Terhune, Chad. (2007, September 14) New Insurance Plan Has Novel Pitch–Get Sick, Buy More. *The Wall Street Journal.*
10. Mercer Human Resources Consulting. (2006) *Beyond Early Adopters: Consumerism at Work in the Marketplace*
11. McQueen, M.P. (2007, August 21) Health Insurers Target Individual Market. *The Wall Street Journal Online.*
12. The Henry J. Kaiser Family Foundation staff. (2003) *Impact of Direct-to-Consumer Advertising of Prescription Drug Spending.* Menlo Park, CA: The Henry J. Kaiser Family Foundation.
13. Gallagher, Kathleen. (2006, April 17) Medical devices a healthy stock pick? *The Milwaukee Journal Sentinel.*
14. Osterweil, Neil. (2005, September 20) *Medical Research Spending Doubled Over the Past Decade.* URL: www.MedPageToday.com
15. Seward, Zachary M. (2007, July 25) Doctor Shortage Hurts a Coverage-for-All Plan. *The Wall Street Journal.*
16. Davis, PhD, Karen and Sara R. Collins, PhD. (Winter 2005/2006) Medicare at Forty. *Health Care Financing Review.*
17. Moore, Judith D. and David G. Smith, PhD. (Winter 2005/2006) Legislating Medicaid: Considering Medicaid and Its Origins. *Health Care Financing Review.*

18. Opensecrets.org. (2006) Lobbying Database. Medical Device Manufacturers Assn. URL: www.opensecrets.org
19. Wilde Mathews, Anna and Rhonda L. Rundle. (2007, July 17) Schwarzenegger Fights to Save Health Plan. *The Wall Street Journal Online.*
20. Staff. (Winter 2005/2006) Key Milestones in Medicare and Medicaid History, Selected Years: 1965-2003. *Health Care Financing Review.*
21. Freudenheim, Milt. (2007, August 30) Patients Turn to No-Interest Loans for Health Care. *The New York Times.*
22. Goedert, Joseph. (2003) *HIPAA's Long and Winding Road.* URL: www.healthdatamanagement.com
23. HIPAAaps.com. (2007) *What is HIPAA? – Background and History.* URL: www.hipaaps.com
24. U.S. Department of Labor. (2007) *Consumer Expenditures in 2005* (Report 998). Washington, DC: U.S. Bureau of Labor Statistics.
25. Reinhardt, Uwe E., Peter S. Hussey, and Gerard F. Anderson. (May/June 2004) U.S. Health Care Spending In An International Context. *Costs and Competition.*
26. Zieger, Anne (Editor). (2007, January 2) *Retail Clinics Keep Advancing.* URL: www.fiercehealthcare.com
27. Reuters Staff. (2007, April 24) Wal-Mart to Open 400 In-Store Clinics in 2-3 Years. *Reuters.*
28. HBJ Staff. (2006, October 12) RediClinic Adds Nine Wal-Mart Medical Clinics in Virginia. *Houston Business Journal.*
29. Gizmag.com. (2007, April 4) *The Emergence of the Convenient Care Clinic.* URL: www.gizmag.com
30. Sullivan, Drew. (2006) Retail Health Clinics Are Rolling Your Way. *Family Practice Management Magazine.*

31. Porter, Sheri. (2007, February 1) *Retail Clinics Sign Academy Agreement.* URL: www.aafp.org
32. Zeiger, Anne (Editor). (2007, May 17) *Walgreen Acquires Retail Clinic Operator.* URL: www.fiercehealthcare.com.
33. Zeiger, Anne (Editor). (2007, June 7) *New Retail Clinic Serves Air Travelers.* URL: www.fiercehealthcare.com
34. McNerney, Tracey (Editor). (2007, March 29) Most Are Satisfied With Care At Retail-Based Health Clinics. *The Wall Street Journal Online.*
35. Zeiger, Anne (Editor). (2007, July 31) *Solantic Urgent Care Clinics Snag $100M Investment.* URL: www.fiercehealthcare.com
36. Moewe, M.C. (2006, April 14) Ex-Columbia Chief Helps Grow Solantic. *Jacksonville Business Journal.*
37. Pachias, Elizabeth M. and Judy Waxman. (2007) *Women and Health Coverage: The Affordability Gap.* New York, NY: The Commonwealth Fund and National Women's Law Center.
38. Girion, Lisa. (2007, October 3) Healthy Living Could Save U.S. $1 Trillion, Study Finds. *Los Angeles Times.*
39. Naik, Guatam. (2007, September 6) In Holland, Some See Model For U.S. Health-Care System. *The Wall Street Journal.*
40. The Advisory Board Company. (2007) *The State of Transparency in Health Care*
41. Cross, Margaret Ann. (2004) Consumer-Directed Plans Begin Measuring Patient Satisfaction. *Managed Care Magazine.*
42. Sensor, Wayne. (2006) *Consumer-Driven Health Care* (White Paper). Alegent Health.

43. Girion, Lisa. (2007, May 28) Doctors List Puts a Price on Care. *Los Angeles Times.*